Colors of WAR & PEACE

A WORK OF CREATIVE NON-FICTION BY

D.M.THOMPSON

Pending Library Of Congress has catalogued the book edition as follows:
Thompson, Daniel, 1946

Colors of WAR & PEACE: A Collection of Short Stories. Lost & Found
Generation, Vietnam/aftermath, Veterans, Buddhism, Plum Village,
PTSD, MACV-SOG, Special Forces Reserve, Mai Loc, Vietnam.

ISBN 978-0-9997286-0-4

Book Cover by Emily Park

DEDICATION

This book could not exist without the memories of so many Special Operations Association (SOA) brothers. Their stories sparked an exploration, squared the circle, where we arrived so long ago. Though connected by war, our experiences were never the same. Perceptions and memories, colored by time, gave each voice its own relentless truth and strengthened my own. For all who shared, I am eternally grateful.

ACKNOWLEDGMENT

Thanks to David Robbins and fellow veterans of The Mighty Pen Project, who inspired and helped shape some of these stories and Major Rachel Landsee for her keen editing. My deep gratitude to Maxine Hong Kingston, Ted Sexauer and the Veteran Writers Group whose friendship, though separated by a continent, kept the circle unbroken. Above all, I give profound thanks to my wife and amanuensis, Mary; whose sharp eye and poetic ear never failed. Her love and support unbending, like Ariadne, guided me through the maze.

CONTENTS

BLUE TATTOO

At completion of the 18th week of OCS training a Senior Status Review and formal dinner party [Ball] culminates 18 weeks of training and the attainment of Senior [Blue] Status.

Headquarters, Department of the Army
DA Pam 601-1

F*irst Call* bugle sounded as boots clopped down three flights of stairs, thoroughbreds posting at the gate. Blue eyes with dark circles appraised the white walls and flattop in full-length mirror. Airborne! I assessed the image, performative and shiny as the gold buckle centered on my gig line. Starched shirt, cardboard flat, bound my exuberance, chafed skin; broad shoulders and small waist. OD fatigues flared, riding pants bloused above spit-shined boots. Black helmet glistened, two fingers fit, nose to rim. After seventeen weeks in a desert of efficiency my well of resilience was bone dry.

Every day was Derby Day in Officer Candidate School. OCs ran hard; put away wet. 82nd Company formation readied, *Stand To,* Reveille, 0630. The same peppy tune my great-grandfather, Johann, heard in 1862 out on the Great Plains during the last Sioux uprising; and my father, Schofield Barracks, December 7th, 1941. From childhood, bugles had structured life; their cadence informed my circadian rhythms.

Standing at parade rest, first rank, front and center, I was exposed to the whimsical pursuit of senior candidates, but further vexed by Lieutenant Harold McGrit's discriminating eye. The sixth platoon tactical officer was assigned in the fourth week of the twenty-four week training cycle. McGrit had replaced Lieutenant Gray. Six weeks later the *Army Times* listed Gray KIA, Vietnam; popup target, non-electric. McGrit always said the average life span for a second lieutenant in Vietnam was as long as a fruit fly. That put us at the end of the larval stage.

I stared across the 8th Battalion parade ground at the two hundred and fifty-five foot jump towers; hypnotized by the incessant wink of red-eyed Cyclops. Their open arms extended one hundred and thirty-five feet, tip-to-tip, head and shoulders above the tree line.

The blinking strobes mocked me; my choice to volunteer for OCS, forego Jump School and the Special Forces training for which I'd enlisted. If boarded out, there would be no Green Beret, Merrill's Marauder's, OSS jumping behind enemy lines. My rebellious nature craved the ideal of self-sufficient insurgency while teetering precariously on this rigid plank of perfectionism. Airborne icons imbued from youth, at once lifted aspirations and loomed as a harbinger of failure.

Washing out now meant reduction in rank to Spec 4th Class and orders for Vietnam, no jump school, no specialized training; reassigned to a line unit, just another dog-faced ground pounder.

Sixth platoon, twenty-two OCs stood ramrod straight as my eyes drifted across 8th Battalion parade ground. I squinted at a pale shaft of light inside a booth, a phone book, battered and lynched, hung by a chain. The lone light, a beacon of hope and sign of despair, fronted on Way Street. It lightened my mood with a promise of reprieve. The Senior Ball was at hand and I was in search of Cinderella.

It turned out even dates were subject to army regulation. Official policy required a Senior Status Review and a date for the formal Officer's Club, *Dining In*. We'd been tested; scrutinized and assessed by spot reports, evaluations, TAC and peer reviews, observations and exams. Finding a date to the Senior Ball rose to the top of my list, along with a hundred others. In this game of endurance, great expectations could be shackled by a thousand details, perfectly executed.

Twenty-two OCs braced for the morning ritual, knights bowing to a construct of mission and efficiency. We'd been systematically fixed by OC doctrine and further emasculated by our TACs. Sometimes "cooperate and graduate" gave way to baser instincts; devour the weak.

Lieutenant McGrit whispered in my ear, "You have a date yet, candidate?"

"Sir, I'm aggressively exploring all avenues of engagement, sir!" It was crunch time. The last peer review and leadership performance appraisals were complete. We had all but earned senior status. But a slip of the lip, attitude, command presence or bonehead move could put you in his crosshairs.

A week before, I stood braced against the wall outside McGrit's office awaiting permission to enter. I gripped the inside straps of my helmet liner so any passing TAC couldn't slap it away. I knocked.

"Enter!" McGrit said. I saluted.

"I want you to compile a list of all building deficiencies," he said, "for the upcoming IG inspection. Every ding, chip, broken tile, loose door knob, cracked window from top to bottom." He wasn't subtle about my motivation. "This task will reflect directly on your next evaluation." Meaning that if I failed to provide him with an exquisitely detailed and actionable report, I could bend over and kiss my Blue ass goodbye.

"You finished cataloging that report?" McGrit said. His bulldog features and premature jowls disparaged a pencil thin neck. After assuming command he'd quickly earned the tag Deputy Dog. But there was nothing cartoonish about his sardonic wit or rabid bite.

"Sir, one more floor to inspect," I said. "I'll need another pass tonight, sir." The truth was I needed to get to that phone booth after lights out to find Cinderella, or at the very least, an ugly stepsister. That pass was my salvation. Here I stood at the crossroads of a fledgling career with daily pressures of survival; exams, ratings, extra duty and this IG list. It wasn't enough that failing out of OCS could radically change my life, but my real stress? Getting a date for the Senior Ball.

"You're hanging by a thread, candidate. I'd better have a complete list by tomorrow morning. Now drop and give me twenty," McGrit said. He pursued our failure through a profusion of orders, objectives and aspirations—mostly his.

McGrit took three paces forward and centered on the platoon. He made clear any misunderstandings we had about "Turning Blue."

"Any man who doesn't have a date of female persuasion, excluding mother or sister, to accompany him to the Officer's Club, will not earn senior privileges. Is that clear!"

"Sir! Yes, *sir!"* The platoon heaved up a full-throated response.

"We're down to twenty-two," McGrit said. His thin lips sagged at the corners, "One to go." This referenced a glib remark he made the first day he assumed command. "I'll be surprised if half this platoon graduates." In the ensuing weeks it morphed into a mantra and finally a maxim, recounted daily as an article of faith.

"Today," throat phlegm rattled, "Today is the last block of bayonet instruction. What is the spirit of the bayonet?"

"To kill!" We roared, *"To kill!"*

"This block of instruction will enhance your ability to train men with the necessary skills to close with and destroy the enemy during close quarter combat. I expect your undivided attention and energetic response. If chosen to participate in *any* demonstration or exercise *you will perform* at your maximum skill level and intensity. You *will* give it your *all*! Is that clear?"

"Sir! YES, *sir!"* Our disparate, Benning School for Boys choir, engendered esprit, promoted aggressiveness that

garnered high ratings from the Tiger Tactics Committee. Every company in five battalions competed for their highest award. It was based on a cumulative set of ratings from all departments that trained and supported OCS. It was evident by the sweat of our brow that Captain Olds, our commanding officer, wanted his Officer Evaluation Report to reflect two achievements; perfect IG inspection score and the Tiger Tactics Award.

"*Any* questions about this training?"

"*Sir!* No, *sir!*"

McGrit ordered open ranks. I took two steps forward; dress right, dressed. By now, other platoons were in the dying cockroach or front leaning rest position. McGrit swaggered between files like a Persian potentate. Candidate Carter's gig line was crooked. "Give me twenty, Pig Pen." Bentley's helmet tilted slightly and rim measured more than two-fingers from his nose. "You a cabby? Give me twenty." Myer's poncho, pressed and folded impeccably over his pistol belt, centered at the base of his spine, lacked a blousing rubber. "Give me fifty." McGrit ripped it off his pistol belt and covered him like a battlefield casualty. Refolding it to exacting specifications could take hours he didn't have.

McGrit stopped in front of Candidate Jeremiah Meeks. He made it his duty to spread misery equally; yet thicker for some than others. He invaded Meek's space. Barely five feet six, Meeks' arms and legs were muscled from high school track. His stocky frame resembled his father, Jebediah, preacher, First African Baptist Church.

"Why haven't you turned in your quit notice Preacher Man?" McGrit glowered.

"Sir, Candidate Meeks is not a quitter, sir," Meeks said. He was compliant, endowed with mental and physical toughness, sharp intellect but rank-less. He did not fit this OC enterprise, true of the vast majority of candidates boarded out. Contrary to aspiration and lore, you weren't forged by army training after you arrived. You'd long been cast to fit its mold.

"Drop and give me fifty!"

Meeks' rounded posture and disdain for tailored fatigues, spit and polish, made him a template of disparity. He was an army of one; parried assault with alacrity. The last IBM punch card ranked him first academically. McGrit scored him soft on leadership, motivation and initiative. His 3.8 GPA at Yale was incidental.

"Uppity!" McGrit said. "I got plans for you."

That Meeks was the last person of color to remain in the platoon proved miraculous. Three other blacks had washed out by week eight, four weeks after McGrit took over. Munoz left the eleventh week; boarded at intermediate status. But Meeks' tenacity matched McGrit's singular resolve, that no nigger or wetback would be commissioned from his platoon. In his official capacity as officer and gentleman he'd never said the "N" word, but his prejudice radiated like the neon sign out front his daddy's general store, Holy Pond, Alabama. We all received special attention, but none so special as Meeks.

Strutting through the ranks, McGrit recounted numerous

infractions and the contagion of lassitude that infected sixth platoon, and 82nd Company in general. If left unchecked, it would result in the breakdown of discipline, esprit and poor group proficiency. He stopped in front of me, nodded and took my measure. "The last six weeks of OCS requires diligence, perseverance, initiative and above all the will to overcome obstacles," he said. "Is that clear?"

"Sir, Yes, *sir!*" I bellowed.

"When fear is replaced by intransigence, unit cohesion is lost and *all* is lost," McGrit said. But we all knew the real obstacle course.

"How blessed is the man who fears *always*," said McGrit. "Isn't that right, Meeks?"

"Sir, Yes, *sir!*" Meeks said. "Proverbs 28, *sir!*"

"Well this is my flock Preacher," McGrit said, "I am the way and the light! Now drop and give me a hundred." McGrit adjourned to the Mess Hall while Meeks pushed up Georgia. I bent sideways and slipped two fingers under his belt and lifted with each count.

After chow, one hundred-forty OCs on the cusp of "Turning Blue," 82nd Company shuffled across the parade ground, starched and spit-shined. Sun sparkled off a sea of black helmets. It wasn't until Candidate Meeks, trained tenor, sang a *Jody call* that files straightened, postures stiffened, men marched in sync:

Around her hair she wore a yellow ribbon
She wore it in the springtime, and in the month of May
And if you asked her why the hell she wore it
She wore it for her soldier who was far, far away

Dust stirred as boots struck the sunbaked earth. Marching past the abandoned phone booth, I inspected its cracked glass. The door, slightly unhinged, absorbed nightly beatings; born of tensions, frustrations and failures to find Cinderella. Good news—the telephone receiver was intact, its silver cord attached firmly to the moneybox. However slim, I still had a chance.

As I looked at the battered booth I recalled the wasted hours waiting in turn, wondering if I'd get lucky. Rumor control said a stable of local talent enjoyed attending Senior Balls. Lists floated around that I hadn't the good fortune to acquire. My luck had turned when McGrit gave me the nightly pass.

The Company posted guards as we crossed Way Street, skirted battalion classrooms and strode into shade. Tall pines blocked blazing sun. A pounding footfall echoed from the wooden bridge spanning Raiders Creek. Turpentine, pine tags, scented the air. Water rushed over ragged rocks and boulders worn smooth.

We marched into sunlight, came to a halt in front of a large pole barn and bleachers. A tin roof covered wooden trusses, boxed on three sides. We filed into the stands with a *can do* crescendo, a low roar that built like *Bolero,* rose in full throated intensity as one hundred and forty voices roared.

A crusty ranger ordered, "Take Seats!"

Sergeant First Class McKay, NCOIC, stood erect, parade rest, black baseball hat, Ranger Tab, roast turkey tan. A white T-shirt pulled tight across chiseled chest. His jungle boots planted on the 4x4 platform to our front. His tightened jaw and fierce eyes made evident he'd eaten rusted nails for breakfast.

Across Ranger Field stood Infantry Hall, six stories, brick and mortar; half million square feet. In the circular loop out front stood Iron Mike; fifteen feet of steel and resin. Frozen mid-stride, charging; steel pot cinched, bedecked in bandoleers, grenades dangling, arm cocked; fixed bayonet. His gaping mouth gave silent cry, commanded 82nd Company, *do or die.*

We'd endured hours of instruction on this field: Drill and Ceremony, PT-daily dozen, sawdust pits, hand-to-hand, bayonet training, killing techniques, and pugil pit.

Pugil training was ostensibly designed to teach technique, imbue the heroic toe-to-toe. We battled in the grit pit; wore protective cups and football helmets. But it had little to do with Olympic ideals. Dominance and aggression were key; survival of the fittest, paramount. Nothing made it easier for a TAC to sort out prejudices than testing an OC's mettle in the pit. The training tapped into the primordial, eat or be eaten core.

"What is the spirit of the bayonet?" McKay's deep, resonant voice called.

"To *kill!* To *kill!*" The roar, amplified by the metal roof, rolled across the field and echoed off Infantry Hall.

McKay, born-again ranger, evangelized a doctrine of skill and pugnacity. "Rigorous training engenders confidence and aggressiveness and infantry esprit!"

A lean buck sergeant posted to our front. "Just back from Vietnam!" McKay said. 82nd Company gave a languid roar.

"On guard!" McKay said.

The gaunt sergeant, angry fishhook-scar on chin, presented with steely resolve. He grimaced, growled, flexed knees and thrust fixed bayonet towards an invisible enemy.

McKay called out a succession of commands: *high port, whirl, long* and *short thrust, parry, horizontal* and *vertical butt stroke, smash* and *slash.* He reviewed each movement for technique and common mistakes; weak thrust or grip, telegraphing. Fishhook's skills, augmented by brute force, were pursued with singular intensity. With each slash or smash it became apparent that behind his eyes dwelt an unseen enemy; each dispatched with deadly precision.

Heat radiating from the metal roof combined with sleepless nights and stagnant air, sent OCs into a bobble-headed stupor. Ranger Fishhook's impressive technique was eclipsed only by the stealthy moves of the sleep monster.

I fought valiantly, eyes stretched wide and snapped upright from a slump when McKay yelled, *"Long thrust and hold!"* But my brain quickly dissolved into a sweaty incubus. Lack of food, long hours, exams and a string of late night IG parties had drained my tank. I dreamed of an oasis with palm trees. A lone red phone booth stood at its center. I desperately searched for quarters, but only found holes in my pockets.

I awoke as Fishhook's short guttural bursts and gnashing teeth, stepped perilously close and executed a thrust that stopped inches short of my nose. Demonstration complete, Fishhook cut his eyes at the listless audience, came to port arms and double-timed behind the stands.

"During this hour of instruction we have reviewed basic bayonet techniques that will enable you, as small unit commanders, to train your men with the necessary skills to close with and destroy the enemy in close quarters combat!" McKay said.

A smattering of applause followed a timorous roar. The company stirred and sniffed the wind. A pogey truck loaded with all things sugar, parked nearby.

"After a 10-minute break we will demonstrate a combat training exercise designed to enhance unit skills and motivate soldiers under your command," McKay said. We lumbered from the wooden bleachers, craving Baby Ruth or Milky Way washed down by cola—a jolt of pure refreshing sugar.

But McGrit and his merry band of TACs punished the company for its sluggish response. The pogey truck beeped and sped away.

Laying in the dying cockroach position I focused on the jump towers. Airborne trainees, lifted by invisible wires, rose beneath rounded hoops and parachutes. I cradled each dandelion as it floated to earth, so tantalizingly close, yet so far from reach. Bone-tired OCs deprived of sugary nutrition, trundled listlessly into the stands.

Fishhook and six rangers posted to our front, pugil sticks

at port arms; bulky canvas sacks attached to each end. They halted and faced the bleachers; white football helmets, canvas diapers, nut cups and hockey gloves.

Fishhook faced the file of six soldiers, each separated by ten feet. On command, McKay said, "Go!" Fishhook trotted towards the first man. *"Long thrust and hold!"* The first man said, as he thrust his pugil forward and froze.

"At *no time* will men in the file counter the movements of the aggressor!" McKay said. This exercise was the equivalent of running football plays at half speed; light contact, nobody gets hurt.

Fishhook countered the thrust with a parry, followed by a slash; went to port arms, side stepped the first man and continued down the file towards the next and so on. Fishhook countered each man's movement as they called out, finished the walk-through and went to port arms. He led the file behind the bleachers.

McKay quickly picked six OC volunteers and sent us to suit up behind the stands. Candidate Rickets, bow-legged bronco rider from San Antonio; Jay, slim accountant type with horn rimmed glasses; Meeks, sturdy and strong; Walters, an AAU swimmer, shaved and tapered with powerful hands; Harrell, fleet-footed quarterback; and me, a zipper with bulky shoulders.

Fishhook eyed us as we donned protective gear. "None of 'em would last two minutes in a fire fight," he said. Embarrassed by his remarks, other cadre shook their heads and turned away.

I tightened my chinstrap as far as it would go. Its sweat-soaked cushions were slick and rank. The sharp plastic edge of the helmet struck my nose when my head turned. I double lapped the V-shaped protective gear around my waist, tightened the belt, donned gloves and picked up a pugil.

I led the file from behind the bleachers, trotted half a football field away from the stands to a small knoll. As we double-timed at port arms, Infantry Hall loomed large in my line of sight. Iron Mike waved with impunity as McKay, perched on his altar, picked up his megaphone and ordered Fishhook front and center. Though he high-stepped like Welsh Guard, 82nd Company only mustered an anemic response.

As we stood on guard, I eyed Fishhook's axis of advance. Knees bent, I swayed on the balls of my feet. My arms felt the heft of the pugil stick as I balanced its padded ends. My weight shifted as I turned my shoulders and thrust the stick, snapped elbows as if throwing a punch. Sweat streaked my face and stung my eyes. I clawed at the canvas cup, recalling the sting of body blows from boxing days; exhausting flurries, punches and counterpunches, jaw rattling from violent strikes.

Fishhook marched, sinewy and sunbaked, halted in front of the first man. Bow-legged Ricketts gripped the pugil lightly as a lariat, called out then executed his move. But Fishhook only marked time, stared glassy-eyed at something beyond the file of OCs; gloves gripping and releasing his stick, he shifted back and forth, shoulders arched and ready to pounce. His eyebrows lifted and fell, as though startled by a burst of automatic fire from the jungle. A blue *Airborne Ranger* tattoo inked one arm; *Born to Die* festooned the other.

Fishhook growled and trotted toward Ricketts. Again he called "*Long thrust and hold!*" Ricketts lunged with his left foot, thrust his pugil stick and froze. Fishhook parried, stepped in and struck Ricketts; rocked him back on his heels. But instead of stopping, as he'd done during the walkthrough, Fishhook threw a series of vicious blows, finished with a vertical butt stroke that clipped Ricketts' chin, snapped his head back and sent him sprawling.

Surprised, a smattering of OCs booed. Fishhook sidestepped Ricketts and trotted towards Jay, pear-shaped accountant, horn rimmed glasses and tinker toy arms.

"*Short thrust and hold,*" called Jay. Fishhook parried and slashed but followed with a flurry of blows, pads thrashing. The canvas sacks drubbed Jay's head and shoulders. The final smash caught him flush in the face and knocked him down. An angry chorus of boos burst from the bleachers; merged with shrill whistles and catcalls. Fishhooks' unrestrained acts of violence awakened deep-seated feelings of abuse, nurtured during the training cycle; embodied by careless restraint. The sleeping giant awoke, rowdy and aggrieved by ferocity unbound.

McGrit's voice sounded in my ear, 'You *will* give it your *all!*' Did that mean taking a shellacking from this maniac?

Jeers only fueled Fishhook's aggression as he drove deliriously into the Preacher. But Meeks slipped and absorbed the glancing blows like a prizefighter. He never countered, but ducked and wove like his father on the Edmund Pettus Bridge.

He finally caught a savage blow that knocked the pugil from his hands. As his knee touched the ground he thrust his arms out wide, unprotected and bowed his head. Fishhook rabbit-punched him as he trotted past.

Fishhook, a tsunami of rage, rose up poised to pound the OC archipelago. Something buckled beneath me. Energy drained from my legs and arms as this force of nature unleashed its fury and I was forced to choose whether to fight or like Meeks, take a knee. A thousand details added up to one "At-ta-boy," summarily erased by one, "Aw-shit." This moment could end in disaster.

Fishhook waded freestyle into Walters' slim frame. It was clear his agenda was no longer about form or fashion. Walters staggered and turned away. The din and roar of 82nd Company exploded into a pitched frenzy. McKay, alarmed by the vicious blows, clicked on his megaphone and shouted *"Stand down!"*

Heedless of his command, Fishhook tore into Harrell. He was further enraged by Harrell's agile footwork and the ease with which he parried blows. Harrell withstood the frenzied thumping until finally, clipped by a vicious butt stroke, stumbled and fell. 82nd Company, angry citizens of Rome, pounded walls and posts, stomped the wooden benches.

McKay jumped from his perch and ran towards the unfolding. Fishhook's red raging face made evident with each thuggish strike, that his unrelenting ferocity would not subside until he destroyed or dispatched whatever threatened him. As he bludgeoned the file of OCs, I was shaken and aroused by what was about to consume me.

I glanced back over my shoulder at Iron Mike's imposing face. His *follow meeeeeeee* plea registered. In that instant, his iron will and two-fold path; close with and destroy the enemy were thoughts made manifest. The *meeeeeeee* was all about action. If molded in his image, then I was his instrument and *meeeeeeee* would *not* be beaten down on *this* or *any* battlefield, today or any other.

In that moment I trusted the outrage churning in my gut. Energy welled and spread through shoulders and arms as one hundred and thirty-four classmates roared; fortifying my rebellious nature. Four TAC officers and McKay sprinted towards the collision, an irresistible force with an immovable object.

The bugle played *Charge* in my head as Fishhook rushed forward. A burst of adrenaline bolstered my resolve. I stepped forward and called *"Vertical butt stroke!"* tossing aside seventeen rigid weeks of perfectionism and stood my ground.

Fishhook's pugil struck my helmet, spun it sideways with a grating sound and I, one-eyed jack, peered through an ear hole. My legs remembered the heavy bag, balancing on the balls of my feet, snapping counterpunches, hooks, shoulder pressing against the duct-taped punching bag.

My weight shifted and I threw a vertical butt stroke, missed and slashed ferociously as he parried. I pivoted and threw a horizontal butt stroke that caught Fishhook flush on the chin. The canvas sack struck his twisted mouth and I followed with a smash to the face. His eyes flashed disbelief as he tilted back on his heels, toppled like a Georgia pine.

I was lifted by the rush and unrelenting roar of 82nd Company as they stomped wooden seats and McKay charged, screaming into his megaphone, "*Stand down*!" as panicked TACs yelled, "*Candidate!!*" I felt my weight shift and shoulders rock, hands and arms powered by pushups struck with such speed and force that Fishhook could only cover up the thrashing. The bugle played on.

McGrit hit my shoulder from the blind side in mid-stroke and spun me away. Fishhook shook his head, rolled on his stomach and tried to push up on all fours. McKay pressed his boot on his back and pinned him to the ground. McGrit screamed into my eyehole, as the other TACs surrounded and led me down the swale to the back of the bleachers. 82nd Company roared, arms pumping, grinning as they smacked each other's back. The revelry continued unabated even after I was ushered past the stands. The TACs order to *"Stand down"* only incited further riot. It was only after individual platoons were ordered to "*Fall in*," they stopped.

As I removed protective gear McKay escorted Fishhook past without a word, arm gripped. Fishhook broke loose and ran yelling, "Which one of you! Which one of you! *I'll kick your ass!*"

"Right here, sergeant!" I called, stepping forward. Fishhook stepped nose-to-nose, shaking and decomposed.

"You wouldn't last five minutes!" yelled Fishhook.

"He didn't have to," McGrit said.

"He didn't follow instructions, *sir!*"

"Got a little carried away, did he, sergeant?"

McKay grabbed Fishhook by the arm. McGrit, baffled and disgruntled, stared while I removed gear and donned my shirt and helmet.

"What *the hell* you thinking, candidate?" McGrit asked.

"Sir, may I speak freely, *sir?*" I picked up the pugil.

"This ain't a democracy, candidate." McGrit said. "Haven't you learned anything since you've been here? What I want . . . what interests me, is what possessed you to incite this riot and beat that ranger like a stepchild." He paused.

"Sir," I searched for Meeks' verbal adroitness, sensitivity or humor and dismissed tact as the school solution. I could begin my response with, 'Sir, there is no excuse for . . .' as was the habit. But those words stuck in my throat like a chicken bone. What the hell? I was done anyway, all that perfection washed away by satisfaction. This was my chance to purge seventeen weeks of tap dancing around the Uniform Code of Military Justice; OCS codes and traditions; orders, oral and written; nitpicking assignments; goals that conflicted with objectives and guidelines; insufficient sleep and food; harassment, subtle and blatant; all in the trivial pursuit of exacting priorities. But then I recalled McGrit's instructions.

"Sir, I was following your explicit orders, sir," I said.

"To what end, candidate?"

"Sir, 'OCS requires the will to overcome obstacles.'"

"What about the Tiger Tactics Award?"

"Sir, I gave it my all."

"Brilliant. Maybe your all was too much! What about

discretion is the better part of valor?" I mirrored his intense stare.

"I guess I'm no fruit fly, sir."

"You may wish you were."

82nd Company formed up and the student company commander ordered us to remove ponchos and put them on. Someone grumbled and I felt guilty about any punishment meted out and wished McGrit had just told me to pack my shit when we got back to the company area so no one else would be subjected to whatever was about to hit the fan.

McGrit addressed the company after we donned our heavy plastic ponchos, draped like smocks, below the knees. We covered our heads with hoods and cinched them tight. McGrit said we all looked hot and tired and should be rewarded.

"You're probably asking yourself, why the poncho?" McGrit said. "Because I don't want you getting wet when you low crawl up Raiders Creek."

TACs drove OC lemmings over the stone wall, crashing into Raiders Creek. But to their unbelieving eyes we responded with wild enthusiasm as we splashed and low crawled, scuffed boots and tore knees and elbows out of our fatigues. And as we low crawled, Meeks called out:

Here we go again
Same old stuff again
Crawlin' down Raiders Creek
Ain't no Ranger we can't beat

This further enraged the TACs. The fact that ordering us into the creek did not produce the usual compliance, piss-ant moans and groans, sent them into a kind of frenzy. The more they yelled the louder we sang. Our collective energy steeled each other's resolve, further bonded us in pain and misery, bolstered our esprit and fueled our pride. When Meeks was yanked aside I took over the *Jody call*, and when I was ordered out of the creek, Ricketts took up the call, then Harrell and so on. This pattern continued, unbroken. The louder we sang the further we crawled, without protest or proviso, at once compliant yet defiant.

Sequestered in the front leaning rest position on the bank of Raiders Creek with Meeks, Ricketts and Harrell, we watched 82nd Company crawl, heartened and undeterred. I realized that in a moment of powerlessness one man's action, or his words can spark an indomitable spirit that welds men together with a torch of the impossible. In that moment there is no individual but a collective of one—indivisible and resilient.

As I looked across Ranger Field at Iron Mike, I understood that leading the charge; doing the right thing regardless of consequence had lit the fuse of determination and cohesiveness. Taking down Fishhook and crawling up Raiders Creek was forever imprinted on our minds and bodies. My actions had ignited a sense of dignity and steeled self-confidence; bound us together as the cohesive unit. After that day, 82nd Company, sixth platoon, was never the same.

Freed from excesses of perfectionism gave confidence to my choices. A body tested in the heat of struggle, keeps the score. I had negotiated the OC maze, one step, one day at a time; layers of SOPs, codes, rules, orders and laws. At its center, Meeks' simple truth revealed. "Rebellion is painful, never efficient, but frees the soul."

Call to Quarters sounded. I finished squaring away cubical but I hadn't time to polish boots or fold poncho. I skipped down the stairs, turned in the IG report and slipped out of the company area. Alone in the phone booth I slapped a handful of quarters on the change ledge and checked the list that had dropped like manna into my hand.

I kept dialing until I was down to my last quarter. It was way past bed check. I looked at an unmarked, unchecked and unadorned name, Johnette Brickhouse. I figured the spelling was wrong and it should be *Jonette*. French, I assumed. Maybe OCs didn't want to call a Johnette out of certain well-established prejudices.

"Major Brickhouse residence," a woman said, with warm measured voice.

My hand shook. I had a live one! I introduced myself and asked for *Jonette*.

"You mean John-ett," she said, "I'm her mother. She won't be home from college until the end of the week."

"I'm Turning Blue, Saturday," I said, "Do you think she would like to attend a Senior Ball at the Officer's Club?"

"I'm sure she'd love to, but I'll have to ask," she said. "Could you call back in a couple of days?"

Jesus! Had I heard right?

"Are you sure?" I asked. Sometimes, after so many *no's*, it's just hard to accept a *yes*.

"It might be a good idea to call a bit earlier," she said.

"I'll try," I said. "But I serve at the pleasure of my TAC Officer."

"I can appreciate that but you don't want to talk to the major at this hour." She laughed.

I had to close the deal. "I'll pick your daughter up at 1800 hours ma'am and have her home promptly."

"She's a junior at *Georgia* for goodness sakes."

"I'll do my best to call Thursday," I said. "Thank you." I opened the door and stepped from the stall of uncertainty into the dark night of possibility. It seemed impossible to calculate the elastic persistence needed to overcome so many obstacles. Fate, faith, will, luck or some combination—I marveled at the starry night.

My boots were shined and poncho folded when I slipped back into the darkened platoon bay. Meeks' bed had been stripped and rolled, locker emptied, all his gear gone. McGrit had fulfilled his final task, purged the enemy from his ranks.

I pulled up in front of a small rancher on Hope Street and knocked on the door. The rich, sweet scent of magnolia, lilac and Old Spice cloyed. As I stood waiting, I glimpsed the red-eyed Cyclops, high above the tree line peering through the dark deciduous leaves, winking as the door opened. A tall, distinguished woman with short brown hair and soft smile invited me in. "I'm Marjorie." She offered a warm hand.

"This is Major Brickhouse," she said. A tall raw-boned officer rose from his smoking chair, shook my hand as he scanned me like groceries at a check out counter; sat and read the *Army Times*. Front page, "238 KIA." He wore short-sleeve khakis, rank with crossed rifles. He was well credentialed, like my father; Combat Infantry Badge and Master Blaster Wings, but without a star.

"Pleased to meet you, sir," I said. He nodded. Dark penetrating eyes and sharp nose made symmetrical his angular face. The paper lifted into a wall.

"It'll just be a moment," she said. "Have a seat."

It was hard keeping my left foot from tapping. It wanted to get the hell out of there. I sat upright on two inches of leather chair. The rest of the furniture I recognized as army issue, just like home.

I checked my watch for the umpteenth time. Major Brickhouse lowered his paper and gave steely-eyed review. "You will be going to Vietnam," he said.

"Yes, sir," I said, "That's a distinct possibility."

"No, that's a certainty."

"Yes, sir."

"A word of caution," he said, summarily. "Vietnam is not Korea or W-W-two. Do you understand?"

"Yes, sir," I said. "Vietnam is an insurgency, designed to disrupt and destroy the South Vietnamese government and civil society through asymmetrical warfare and by means of force multipliers such as terrorism and guerrilla warfare." I had learned all this in Infantry Hall, where every class began with,

"If you don't learn the principals taught during this block of instruction, you will die in Vietnam!" To which we all pounded on our desks and cheered. Gallows humor.

"Yes and no," he said. His stern eyes admonished. "What I mean is—don't be a hero." Which, as he turned back to his paper, left this newly appointed senior candidate perplexed. I'd been on an eighteen-week pilgrimage, partook of the SOS sacrament and low-crawled the holy waters of Raiders Creek; stood at the feet of Iron Mike. His words verged on blasphemy.

Mrs. Brickhouse reappeared and said Johnette would be out shortly. Sitting here after eighteen long weeks in my starched khakis, spit-shined low quarters, blue epaulets with AG-344 cap, I knew the apple didn't fall far from the genetic tree. I wondered which Brickhouse would walk through that door; hatchet-faced Johnett from her father's branch, or Jonette the French mademoiselle from her mother's side?

She emerged, a vision of loveliness in a black sleeveless shift, fashionably cut above her knees that tastefully accentuated her blue eyes, blond hair and tan athletic body. Her faint mischievous smile conceded feminine gamesmanship . . . *but as you can see, I'm worth the wait.* To which I nodded agreeably . . . *you have no possible idea.*

As we entered the O' Club I was a Prussian Prince, and she, Alexandrine, by my side. The reception line greeted her like royalty. McGrit nodded, cast approving glances as I presented her to the commander and his wife. My stock was rising.

I'd won the jackpot for the most beautiful woman at the ball, hands down. Later, I felt stares of approval and envy from

OCs and TACs as McGrit squinted, stood alone in a corner near the bar nursing a drink. As I described the characteristics, uses and deployment of enfilade fire, *Jonette* nodded attentively, held my gaze and touched my arm lightly.

That first Blue night of my eighteenth week, I realized it wasn't fear but the rewards of struggle that got you to Hope Street. An innocent kiss and firm embrace beneath a dim porch light, the faint whiff of Jolie Madame and a soft reassuring touch was more than ample reward. As she closed the door with a coy wink, the treble notes of the bugle call *Tattoo*, inescapably haunting, alerted my ear. By tradition, it was the same sound that urged innkeepers to send horse soldiers from town back to garrison—and so it did, my first *Blue Tattoo*.

WALKING POINT WITH SERGEANT ROCK

1.

I slipped and belly-flopped in red mud, rifle in one hand, flashlight the other. Huddled in a leaky bunker, a Bru Montagnard pondered my precarious plight. I rolled on my back, pointed the red filtered flashlight at my face; pounded it against my thigh then extended it arm's length. It blinked behind a waterfall and came to life. A thin indige poncho wrapped my skeletal remains. The poncho hood, cinched tightly into a small, irregular circle, covered my head. Bulky web gear, LBE suspenders, ammo pouches, canteen, draped my coat-hanger shoulders.

MLT-1, Mobile Launch Team–One, sat next to a rutted airfield ten klicks south of Camp Carroll, a Marine stronghold on Highway 9. It was plopped down between the Vietnamese village of Mai Loc and a Montagnard village. SOG recruited SCU, Special Commandos, from the Bru village. The Viet Cong males of Mai Loc, between sixteen and sixty, emerged nightly, wore black pajamas; planted mines and booby-traps along roads and trails.

First General Order: *Guard everything within sight and hearing.* That was easy. The small launch site would fit into a 7-Eleven parking lot. I was charged with making nightly rounds, checking SCU along the perimeter. Montagnards, French for mountain people, were a handsome indigenous race with Malayo-Polynesian features and Hawaiian skin. Their crossbow culture had been dragged into twentieth century killing fields. Having jumped from stone-age weaponry to M-1 rifles, times grew curious and complex. A crossbow needed no lubricant and arrows didn't jam in the ejector assembly. Place arrow on string, pull, set cocking lever, aim and squeeze. Silent death.

August 1968, MLT-1 stood on alert. Intelligence informed that a North Vietnamese Army Regiment was lurking about the countryside, eyeing this tasty morsel. The same NVA Regiment had overrun Special Forces A Camp, 101 at Long Vei, in February. In the aftermath, remnants of the camp were reconstituted and moved to Mai Loc. Newly built and fortified, A-101 anchored one end of the airstrip while MLT-1 sat loosely tethered at the other.

MLT-1 lay exposed in a valley dominated by the Annamite Range. The backbone of South East Asia, its sclerotic spine curved between Laos and Vietnam. The Ho Chi Minh Road, an engineering marvel, was carved out of this treacherous terrain.

MLT-1, Studies & Observation Group (SOG) launch site,

was a hodge-podge of rusted connex containers, tin roofed bunkers, and moldy GP tents, sagging like green braziers. A darkened doorway in a red mound led underground to the TOC, Tactical Operations Center. Varying lengths of antennae spiked from its slick crown. The nearby 4.2 mortar/Jacuzzi pit was filled with brown bilge, pooling in pouring rain. A combat volleyball net sagged like a potbellied pig. Barbed and concertina wire, trip flares, toe poppers, claymores, and bouncing-betty's wrapped the porous perimeter.

The jerry-rigged camp had been cobbled together by Major Clyde Sincere after FOB-3 and the marines abandoned Khe Sanh. Clyde had thick red eyebrows and dromedary disposition. With the move came the new and improved, Mobile Launch Team concept and name change, MLT-1. Like most new and improved products it had the same utility, just cost more.

Logistically, MLT-1's small airstrip served to refuel helicopters and launch top-secret Recon teams (RTs) across the border into Laos. Tactically, Bright Light teams or Hatchet platoons were launched to retrieve RT remnants, pinned down or overrun. From above, the airstrip looked like a Gauguin painting, bold red stripe splashed across a profusion of green.

2.

As I sloshed between bunkers, the distant report of big guns, 175 mm Long Toms, pulsed with the crisp efficiency of a marine band. I slipped and slammed—arms stretched wide, chest smacking. I rolled and cradled my rifle, retrieved the flashlight. My arms and legs were smeared with clay and except for saran wrap poncho, LBE and flip-flops, I was bare-ass naked.

With the first deluge of monsoon I'd abandoned military issue inside the wire. Gone were wet socks that rubbed feet raw and the sponge-soaked fatigues. No more underwear that bunched into crack and crevice; chafed the crotch. Gone too the caked jungle boots that hardened into ortho plaster.

No matter what the raingear, you were soaked in seconds. I chose the thin, translucent, indigenous poncho for its ease of movement and elegant fit. The cellophane wrap retained no body heat, but it was lighter, quieter and far more pliant than the bulky U.S. Army rubberized poncho. Splashing forward, my sphincter spasmed and a warm discharge spilled down my legs.

August in the highlands resembled autumn in the Adirondacks. The penetrating rain taunted chilblains and pruned fingers. With each step came the slurp of sludge. I wrested a foot from the suck and a flipper was gone. I noodled the muddy hole up to my elbow and wrestled it free.

The life of a bush-tailed lieutenant resembled a first year intern out of med school. The physically demanding duty, grueling hours, monotony, and sleepless nights, were interrupted by frenetic bursts of violence. Any time the chief resident showed up, you'd better have your shit together.

Second lieutenants, goats on the Special Forces totem pole, had to earn their *stripes*, much as a snot-nosed PFC—but there was a catch. There were no slots in Special Forces Table of Organization & Equipment (TO&E) for either. Though qualified by training I lacked experience and rank for this *Top Secret,* Davy Crockett adventure. Recon teams were sent on risky 'sneak and peak' missions, deep into Indian country. By 1968 many of the experienced team leaders, One Zeros, were missing, wounded, dead or just plain burned out. Slots needed to be filled and TO&E be damned. I was proud and humbled to have been volunteered as cannon fodder for this prestigious unit but mostly for serving with these savvy warriors. Their bravery was legion, mission impossible.

I slid to a halt at a leaky bunker and shined the flashlight. Bru squatted, eyes transfixed; as red light filled gaps in toothless grins. Brown sluice slid down the back of my exposed legs. The combination of dysentery and malaria pills caused food and liquid to roar through the alimentary canal. By the end of my first month I'd purged twenty pounds from a raw and ravaged blowhole. Nothing plugged the rush, which at times like now, breached amid step. Hard rain flushed the skunk-works.

As I glanced into the last bunker a Bru gunner alerted. He leaned forward squinting, scanning the minefield. His hands wrapped the spade grips of a .50 caliber machine gun. He pointed its sleek tapered barrel at movement in the minefield as thumbs pressed the butterfly trigger. The pop-sizzle of a flare ignited his suspicions and the stocky Bru jacked back the operating lever and seated a round. White light illumed; shadows shifted on a smoky curtain. Rounds exploded from the machine gun as heavy metal, *In-A-Gadda-Da-Vida, chunk,*

chunk, chunk, pulse; droned on. The jackhammer recoil lifted and shook the small Bru.

Barefoot, I scaled the sand bags to a makeshift tower, searched for the breach, sappers low crawling with satchel charges. My foot struck a metal palette and ripped a hole. Bunkers down the line opened up in quick succession. Hand flares rushed skyward, popped and drifted eerily above the clouds. Voices cried out, tents emptied and every man scrambled.

I clambered up the sandbags in time to see Mango, a mongrel pup, explode with a deafening roar. Shrapnel whizzed past as the .50 cal led a chorus of automatic rifles, machine guns; punctuated by explosions. I slid down the sand bags, dove through the door, grabbed the .50 cal ammo belt and twisted. The base stopped strummin' but the band kept hummin'.

"Cease fire! Cease fire!" The wide-eyed Bru grinned righteously and slumped back against the sandbags. Rain spit and sizzled on the barrel.

I grabbed an aluminum tube tucked in my web belt; removed the firing cap assembly, checked the red cork seal, and slammed the pop flare hard against the palm of my hand. A small rocket whooshed skyward. The eerie glow further spooked Bru machine gunners whose tracers rose, wriggling snakes, swallowed by clouds. The thunderous *ponk* of a four-duce mortar round boomed from the mortar pit. The magnesium flare burned dimly above swirling clouds.

I hustled over to the TOC and reported the puppy threat

terminated with prejudice. An all clear sounded. After the inquisition and diatribe by a crapulent West Point captain, the mortar tube was plugged, weapons cleared, and soldiers fell abruptly into monsoonal malaise. The Bru gunner sulked, saddened by the loss of a culinary delight.

3.

A sliver of light broke on the horizon. There was just enough time to clean my weapon, get chow, saddle up and report to the TOC for patrol. Something niggled, or maybe that hollow feeling in the pit of my stomach meant I was running on fumes.

I secured the tent flap tight against the rain. A row of folding cots covered with field mosquito nets lined the isle. I flipped the waterlogged tarp that covered my cot. Water plashed on soggy floor. The cramped quarters discouraged segregation of officers from non-coms.

"Jesus," SFC Short said, "Haven't you done enough damage for one night?" He chuckled and rubbed his shaved head. Everyone called him Short Round, but he was neither short nor round.

Shit runs down hill in the army; not surprisingly, low man on the pole stayed ankle deep. Had no time for banter. I found a field chair, sat and examined my mud-caked foot. Blood dripped from the gash.

"The old man pissed?"

"XO chewed my ass." I pulled gauze and tincture of iodine from my ammo pouch; cleaned and covered the gash with a butterfly bandage then looked around for tape.

"One casualty," Short Round said. "El-Tee Boykin fell in the mortar pit and broke his leg!"

"Raining so hard you can't see a hand in front of your face."

"While you're traipsing round the countryside, I'll be digging out that base plate!"

"Got any tape?" I squeezed the pad of my foot.

"What's that smell?" Short's muscular legs hung from his cot. His thick arms braced his upper body while a mosquito net draped his shoulders like a kafiya.

"Burnt rope." Hemp, I thought. I looked toward the empty cots at the back of the tent. Maybe some medicinal weed would settle my stomach.

"Smells like shit!" Short studied my see-through duds.

My stomach cramped; sphincter twitched. I pulled a bottle of paregoric from my rucksack and took a healthy swig. The camphorated tincture of opium warmed my stomach; shot up my spine and lifted the skullcap. I peeled off the sleek poncho.

"Paregoric?"

"A finger in the dike." It didn't plug the hole so I double dosed.

"Easy does it, El-Tee."

I nodded absently, reached beneath my cot and dragged out a suitcase. Its cheap laminate sides were swollen and separated. My father had lugged it home from his war, as I would from mine. Wrapped heavily with duct tape, the latches were sprung. It was more totem than tote-able.

It made a loud metallic *clunk* as I sat it on a rickety field chair. Though numb, my fingers felt its squishy texture. There was little time before patrol so I resisted the growing urge to cut the tape and open it. Once a daily distraction, with titivating allure: the urge swelled into obsession.

Clearing your head could be tricky, when tedium poured hard as rain. I'd conjured up a diversion; pitted will against temptation, discipline over assent. The game was a mind teaser; dissolved distractions and sharpened focus. But the grueling regimen, the runs and inability to repair, provoked an urge to cut the tape, indulge the impulse.

"What you got there, El-Tee?" Short asked.

"I can't get no, sa-tis-faction," I sang. The double shot of paregoric elevated my desire. I pulled my K-bar and flicked its edge; hesitated, then cut two strips and peeled them off. I bound my foot with one strip.

"Get Doc to check that before you go out."

"Gotta go." I slid the case beneath the cot.

"Maybe you should secure that in the TOC."

"No time."

"Things disappear around here."

More people than things, I thought. "I'm not one of 'em."

Beneath the thin, translucent skin of my fingers was the faint outline of bone. Though melting away, I was grateful for paregoric and mind games. I donned boots, fatigues and jungle sweater, pulled out the bulky U.S. rubberized rain poncho and laid it with my web gear and ruck. With the second strip of tape I wrapped the sling swivels on my rifle and covered the flash suppressor. I squirted a generous load of lubricant over the bolt, though I heard the mocking voice of my drill sergeant warning 'I'll kick any man's ass I find doing that.'

Short Round unbuttoned the tent flap. "Be careful out there today, El-Tee."

"Break a leg?"

I buffed the barrel to an oily sheen; pulled back the charging handle, pulled the trigger and listened for the tinny, firing pin click. "You can tell it's swell, it's Mattel." The same people who made my first cap gun and Shoot'n Shells, made my rifle. The caps didn't fire if they were wet; neither did the M-16.

My thumb depressed the spring inside the twenty-round magazine (subject to jam if more than eighteen). I banged the clip hard against the heel of my hand, seated the 5.56 rounds then flipped the selector switch to S-*lock and load*; raised the tent flap and stepped into the downpour.

The tuberous TOC, center of camp, resembled a red and runny chancre sore. Inside, Major Sincere studied maps spread over table. Aeronautical charts and topos plastered the wall. Magnetic bearings, azimuths, lines were drawn to various firebases.

I took down call signs, radio frequencies and alternatives. The patrol order; out five clicks, look around, and come back home. The surly major stared at me. "You'll be going out with Sergeant Garland." Sincere spread misery evenly like peanut butter on B-2 crackers.

SFC Garland had served three tours. His chiseled cheekbones, three-day beard and square jaw resembled *Sergeant Rock,* whose iron fist could knock out a T-54 tank.

Gathered in the dank underground around Sincere; Sergeant Rock, Short Round, Matson, demolition specialist, the radio operator, pudgy XO and me.

"I've coordinated with the Ruff-Puff, A-101, and marines, about patrolling this area," Sincere said. He circled a spot on the map five kilometers east of the camp. "Enemy activity reported here."

"I patrolled that area two weeks ago," Rock said. "Nothing but rice paddies, hedge rows, and buffalo." Sincere cast a withering gaze. Rock braced but never blinked.

"What about marine patrols?" Rock asked.

"The walking dead?"

"Fuckin' jarheads see Bru, they'll fire us up."

Sincere nodded. "But that would be friendly fire."

"Any gun ships on call?" Rock asked. "Med-e-vac?"

"Not with this ceiling," Sincere said. "Sergeant Short will be on the four-deuce mortar if you run into trouble."

Short winked. "Pin point accuracy," he said. He removed an M-16 plotting board from its case and laid it on the table. He patted the bulky board with white plastic sheet, circular grid, azimuth disk and range scale arm for plotting targets.

Rock eyeballed the objective. "That's maximum range for the four-deuce."

"And your point?" Sincere bared teeth and clamped down on his cigar.

"First of all, *sir*," Rock said, "the propellant ain't all that stable in rain." He challenged the major with a mixture of sarcasm and respect. "Second; four-deuce rounds at maximum distance can deviate wildly and third . . ."

"Do the best with what you've got," Sincere said, "I need to know who's out there and when they're coming."

Rock shook his head. Short shrugged. I remembered the marine batteries firing from Camp Carroll. I listened to them during breaks or late at night when I couldn't sleep. They had two Fire Direction Control centers, battalion and battery.

"How about Camp Carroll?" I asked.

Sincere ignored the question. "Your job, lieutenant, is to hump Sergeant Garland's radio. He's in charge of this patrol. Is that clear?"

Considered a straphanger with only five or six patrols, Uncle Sam had invested a lot of money and training building this ego; further eroded by rain and the runs. I'd graduated from In-Country Orientation Course, making me a COCk qualified officer for Christ's sake! Sergeant Garland was a sergeant. What didn't the major understand? This objection sped through my brain and lit a neon sign on my forehead. Sincere bared his teeth and drew close. "Is that *clear,* lieutenant?"

In this elite unit, 2nd lieutenants were viewed with great suspicion, but carrying a radio for a sergeant was . . . well, beneath me. My ass spasmed and I let loose silent but deadly gas.

Sincere scowled. "Who shit?" I shrugged. Short Round coughed, Matson gagged. The crapulent XO pinched his nose.

"Listen and observe," Sincere said, "and maybe you won't go home in a body bag!" He removed the chewed cigar and spat.

"Yes, sir," I said. I retrieved the PRC-25, checked

frequencies, grabbed extra batteries, and folded my map.

Matson, pen in hand, walked to his calendar, a naked girl with perky tits. Considered a short timer, he intended to cross off the day.

"You sure you want to do that?" Rock asked.

"Got a problem?"

"Never count time til it's locked in the safe," Rock said, "tuck it away and forget the combination."

"What the hell does that even mean?" Matson asked, "Where do you get this shit?" He tossed the pen on the table and instead, patted her perky tits.

On the sly, after they left, I asked the radio operator for call signs and frequencies for Camp Carroll FDC; flipped through the SOI. I mounted the steps. It'd stopped raining and that had to be a good sign.

4.

Sergeant Rock formed up the platoon of SCU. Two Bru strikers from first squad walked point. Nip, thin and gangly, wore a boonie-hat, camouflage rip-stock, wide brim pushed back on his head. Flat-faced Nok wore a fatigue shirt, buttons missing, baggy pants and boots untied. Both had wide, fearless smiles. Rock gave an underhanded wave to move out; as if swatting a ball player on the ass. Nip and Nok led, followed by Meng, the indige platoon sergeant. A veteran of French Follies, he had two missing fingers. I followed Rock, and Matson brought up the rear with third squad.

We marched through the gate and down the far side of

the rutted strip. I followed close into the scrub until we were out of sight. Rock stopped and two columns took a knee, M-1 carbines at the ready.

"El-Tee," Rock said. "Your whip antenna is waving like a semaphore." He pulled the radio out of my rucksack and stuck it in his. He molded the flex antenna down the side of his ruck and secured it with duct tape. "Snipers shoot RTOs. Forget what anyone else tells you—always carry your own radio." He looked around at the Bru, "This radio is your lifeline. Lose control and you're in deep shit."

"Copy that, sarge."

Rock looked at my map. "Where are we?"

"Right, here."

"Where're we going?"

I checked coordinates and pointed.

"How we getting there?"

I drew a line with my finger—A to B.

"Not exactly," Rock said. "The Ruff-Puff, marines, A-camp—god only knows who has intel we're coming. That's why we went south from the camp and circled back into the bush." Rock pulled out a shiny map covered with acetone, four grease pencil lines zigzagging. "Vary your route, don't be predictable. Stay off the trails. Now get up there with the first squad and take us to this first point."

"What about the major?"

"Doin' the best I can with what I got."

Well there it was, I'd gotten my wish to lead men; most of whom were technically boys; SCU in their early teens toting

M-1 carbines, not BB-guns, who could shoot your eye out.

"Follow me," I said. Rock shook his head and donned his rucksack.

Directly to my front, Meng carried a thumper, M-79 loaded with buckshot. In front of him, point men Nip and Nok carried M-1 carbines but no grenades. The Bru, having never played little league, threw like girls.

I shot an azimuth along the first zig as Rock made commo-check. I pointed the direction to Meng and moved out. We marched through the rolling countryside, emerald patties, thick hedgerows, but stayed hidden in scrub, thick patches of vegetation and stands of eucalyptus.

5.

We slogged for hours, through intermittent squalls until we approached the objective. Something wasn't right. My soaked map didn't match up with the rolling terrain. Rock and Meng looked on as I shot back azimuths. Matson stayed in place with third squad. I pointed to where I thought we were.

"Close enough," Rock said. Maps weren't all that accurate. Printed at the bottom: *Karte von Tong, 1954, Cochinchine.*

"What we looking for?" I asked.

"You'll know if you see it."

We trudged on; reached a dike that wound between two paddies, hill one side and hedgerows on the other, perfect for mischief. As we rounded a bend, Meng threw up his hand. I knelt and signaled SCU to point rifles toward the brush, half up the hill, half into the hedgerow. Everything grew quiet.

Rock scuttled forward. "What cha'got?"

Firecrackers, AK-47 rounds, sputtered and cracked overhead. Meng pointed across an open field at bunkers, dirt mounds with firing ports, connected by trenches.

Rock's face went slack. "That ain't good." Another burst of small arms fire snapped overhead. We moved further down into a ditch.

"Beau-coup VC," said Meng. "Koc-a-dow."

Rock radioed, "Jack Black this is Chicken Little . . . one round, Willy Pete." Rock gave coordinates for the fire mission." I listened. "I know you're at *max range*," he yelled. "That's *your* fucking problem!"

But that wasn't exactly true. Once Short dropped that eighteen-pound mortar round down the tube, it was our fucking problem. As we waited for the first marking round the SCU aimed peashooters toward avenues of approach. I placed two SCU further up the hill. Matson formed third squad into a horseshoe and set out a claymore. "Shot out," Rock said. As we waited for the splash of a white phosphorous marking round, I pictured Short—a one man FDC, calculating range and azimuth along the gun target line, deflection and elevation, cranking the elevating gear handle, checking the M-53 sight unit, marking charges, then dropping the round. This took a precious long time.

'Splash' was the estimated time for the shell to hit. It came and went. No shell streaked overhead; sight nor sound of Willy Pete. The round was either short or misguided. I remembered training; how to make mud if a buddy was hit with Willy Pete.

Phosphorus burned as long as it was exposed to oxygen—right through bone and sinew—dropped out the other side of your ass and kept burning through to the other side of the earth. If you didn't have water you had to muster up a good piss. Good thing we had plenty of both.

Rock radioed for another marking round. "Shot out!" The SCU fidgeted; curious as to why explosive rounds weren't raining down.

"No sweat," I said. A burst of automatic fire strafed the top of the ditch.

There was a muffled explosion somewhere south but no sign of smoke. Rock called in the adjustment, "Add 400."

I watched for movement along the trench lines. Another burst came from the wood line. Either the shooter—or shooters—had been left behind to observe the complex or lure us into an ambush. A shell exploded and Willy Pete rose up, sent its tentacles shooting out from that very same spot in the wood line. I hoped Charlie could muster a good piss for his buddy about now.

"Fire for effect," Rock said. Four rounds exploded, splintered trees. Screams came from the burning wood line.

The camouflaged bunkers were solid, well positioned with good fields of interlocking fire. The unseen enemy, hunkered down, waited patiently. I was lightheaded, hadn't eaten, couldn't drink, barely think, and my ass was twitching which meant the medicine was wearing off. I considered taking another swig but thought better of it. Rock drew up a sandlot play on the ground.

"This don't make sense," Rock said. "El-Tee—take first squad down that embankment and set up a line of supporting fire along that dike. Matson, take third squad along that hedgerow. I'll take second squad and have a quick look-see and we'll get the hell outta here!" The bunkers were a good football field away.

"Whoa! Across that field? You don't have fire support, sergeant." It was one thing for Sergeant Rock to take out a bunker singlehandedly in the comics, but this was the real deal and somebody was going to get fucked up.

"Our orders . . . "

" . . . were to recon," I said, "Not assault a bunker complex."

"I'm in command here, *sir*," Rock said.

"You got the radio," I said. "You need 5 to 1 ratio to take a built up position and we've got no fucking idea how many there are." I was out on a limb, going against direct orders—either way was suicide. But maybe Sincere would only hang me up by my balls.

"We've got to move, *now*," Rock said.

"I've got the call sign and frequencies for Camp Carroll, FDC."

"Are you fucking crazy," Rock said. "Who do you think the camp is named after? Carroll was killed by friendly fire!"

"Worse than enemy fire?" I asked. "Dead is dead."

"Those big guns could blow us to smithereens."

"Suggest you radio Short and tell him to stack extra sheets of propellant on the shells," I said. "That should give the rounds another 50-100 meters. We need to keep their heads down until we get out of here. We can always come back."

"I'm running this show, *lieutenant!*"

"Your call, but that's my vote, sergeant," I said, "I'm just a straphanger." But things got iffy in Special Forces when shit went sideways and officers were in the mix. Hell, we were commissioned to take responsibility. Pin it on a 2nd louey.

Rock radioed Short about the extra propellant. "Fuck your tube. We need it now," Rock said.

The rounds came whistling in, exploded fifty meters short of the bunkers. "Add five-oh!" Rock said. He pressed his ear to the handset. "We're done. He breached the tube."

We made an orderly withdrawal as rain began. It had started and stopped so many times I said fuck it and went without the heavy rubberized poncho. Too bad I hadn't taken my indidge poncho. We traipsed through the rolling countryside, made a circuitous loop toward MLT-1. Meng switched out Nip and Nok on point, they fell in line behind me, followed by three Bru from first squad. Rock followed with second squad and Matson brought up the rear. My map turned to paper mache. Flustered by the thought that I could be temporarily disoriented, I forged on.

A blue patch of sky broke open to the east as I scanned the lush vegetation. Glancing back, Nip and Nok ditty-bopped; rifles slung over shoulders like English barons after a hunt. I gestured to carry them at the ready. They smiled. No harm could come—they weren't walking point.

The countryside rose and dropped, undulating and caused a gap to open between the point men and the main column. The accordion movement, expanding, collapsing, and exertion to pull them back in, sapped what energy I had left. If unattended, the unit could split. I quick-stepped up the trail; closed the gap with the front element, turned and gave a hand and arm signal, *double time*, pumped my arm up and down. Nok hiked up his pants and mimicked my gesture, still smiling. I signaled the front element to 'halt.' The point men took a knee. Meng walked passed me as I pointed back to the laggards and the break in the file.

I turned, took several steps and an orange light wrapped me like a wave. A brain-rattling fist slammed from behind and launched me effortlessly. Pain stabbed both eyes, rattled my skull and all went black. The sky spun lazily above—or was it me? Floating, bodiless and empty, I became disoriented.

Tranquility ended with a thud as I crashed to earth, lungs screaming, gasping for air. Somewhere sirens wailed, as vice grips squeezed. My eyes blinked; high speed shutters clicking. Panning the view, all but Rock was a blur. Where was I? What the fuck happened?

"Okay!" A tinny voice echoed inside. I tried to stand, wobbled, and fell to my knees. I felt punch drunk; fifteen rounds of rope-a-dope.

Rock moved to the next casualty as I gathered up. Meng lifted a hand with only an index finger and thumb. Already missing two, a piece of shrapnel had clipped the middle one clean. He stared at the smooth white knucklebone; glanced around and reached for what looked like a tootsie roll. Whittled down by war, he clasped it with his good hand and held tight. I offered morphine but he shook his head.

Vegetation spread concentrically from a large crater. Nip had triggered the booby trap. The broad leaf foliage was blown sideways and folded back, its red speckled underside exposed. An arm wedged high in a stand of bamboo, finger pointing like a washroom sign towards the crater.

Matson arrived, panting, "No fucking way to die!" he yelled. "Jesus! Bits and fucking pieces!" He checked me quickly and returned to his squad.

I struggled to right myself as Rock tied off Nok's leg and got an IV going. The bleeding stopped but the mangled leg would have to come off. His eyes were empty and smile wiped clean. I shot him up with a morphine syrette as Rock checked the defensive perimeter and radioed for a medevac. If we couldn't get one we'd have to haul him back.

I helped indidge scavenge body parts hidden beneath the foliage and stuffed them into the body bag. All I could hear was the major's voice, "And maybe I won't have to send you home in a body bag." Shaken by the explosion my brain clicked off and autopilot on.

The undeniable snap and pop of rotor blades; *Dustoff*, grew in the distance. As Nok's stretcher was lifted onto the chopper, Matson slid the body bag onto the floor. Meng stepped on the skid and sat, feet dangling; his thumb and index finger pointed toward the sun.

As the sky closed in, the wash of rain was comforting. Rock came forward and eyed the spit-wad map clenched in my shaky hand.

"For future reference, you don't give morphine to an amputee!" he said. "You look like shit El-tee. Maybe you should'a got on that chopper."

"Maybe I should'a . . . but I didn't," I said. He took out a dry, clear, acetone covered map and shot an azimuth. "*Fall in!*"

We started the long trek back. But now, walking behind Rock was no guarantee my next step wouldn't send me splintering across the countryside. My comic book faith was shaken. With the randomness of death, I willed each tentative step, denied all attachment and erased Nip and Nok. The day unfinished, I couldn't lock time up and tuck the past away.

6.

I followed Rock as he dismissed the platoon of Bru and headed towards the TOC. The mortar pit was littered with shell casings and the mud-splattered tube ballooned like bubble gum. Its base plate had been driven so far into the ground as to render useless any of Short Round's calculations. Major wasn't around so the armchair quarterback debriefed us.

"What the hell happened?" XO asked.

Rock recounted the patrol; bunkers, mortar, two wounded and one KIA. He pointed to the map. "Fortified with trench works," Rock said. "No artillery or air support."

The XO looked at me. "So you've got nothing to show for a busted mortar, two wounded and one dead?" he asked.

"Sergeant Garland executed the patrol order, found bunkers and suffered casualties from a booby trap," I said. The debrief was drifting towards the army tradition of *pin the fuck up on the donkey*, and I was the nearest ass. "The 4.2 mortar was in support, but remained under MLT command and control." I said.

"Who asked you?"

"I believe you did, sir," Rock said.

I walked to my tent, removed equipment and laid down my weapon. I pulled the paregoric from my rucksack and took a nip. The medicine took the edge off but I needed something more than mind games to prevail. I pulled the suitcase from beneath my cot and took out my K-bar. The blade cut the tape and I lifted its top.

Two twenty-five pound plates fit perfectly squared in the suitcase. On top were two ten-pound plates and dumbbell bars. The side pockets were stuffed with rolled newspaper. It may as well have been a chest of pirate's gold.

"Dumbbells?" Short said. "Jesus, sir, you hauled weights all the way from the states?" I hadn't seen him lying in his cot.

"You breach that tube?" I asked.

"That's what you've been hiding under your bed?"

He gave a dubious look. I brushed the elevated letters and a thousand pinpricks radiated through my fingertips. No words could have expressed why I'd hauled that suitcase halfway around the world. As I lifted the steel plate, a notion came, provoked by muscle memory. The steel was real and so was I.

Two twenty-five pound plates fit one small barbell. I sat squarely on the field chair and gripped the bar. I strained to curl it to my chest. The exquisite pain tore at my muscles as gravity took hold. As momentum waned, my arm stalled and shook uncontrollably. Muscles burned hot and the plates splashed into mud.

I looked around at Short, his thick forearms and barrel chest. He drew close. "This is going to save your ass, El-Tee?" He bent down and removed the two large weights from the bar and replaced them with two ten-pound weights. "Try that."

My arm twitched and strained, burned hot and failed again. Short took off the two weights and handed me the bar. "Sometimes it's good to find our limitations, sir." He pushed through the tent flap and stepped into the rain.

7.

I beat the dysentery, finished two tours and followed Sergeant Rock's advice. After finishing my time, I tucked it safely away and forgot the combination. Years later as life unraveled, "wife, house, kids . . . the full catastrophe," I found myself fixing a leaky pipe in a stank-ass basement, smelling oddly reminiscent of a TOC. I moved a box and there, sealed with tape, the suitcase I'd carried home, just like my father. I cut the thick duct tape and lifted the lid. The scent of gun oil, rust, and moldy earth wafted up, unloosed a flood of memories; Mai Loc; monsoon, dysentery, Nip and Nok—always smiling, Meng—pointing at the sun. I slid two plates on the rusted bar and curled it until my muscles screamed 'Stop!' But muscle memory, my savior—kept pumping.

BOXCAR ORANGE

> In battle, since shields were worn on the left arm, the right flank, right of the line, had to be the strongest.
>
> *Enemies Without and Within*
> T. L. Gore

September 1969, two months into my second tour in Vietnam, I won the lotto. It wasn't clear whether my unit, CCN had gotten an extra allocation for R&R—more likely a recon team had been hit, turned up missing or someone was KIA. If it were the latter, I reasoned, they had already taken flight to paradise. All I knew was, at the last minute I'd gotten a slot for R&R to Sydney, Australia. It was like winning the Irish Sweepstakes without buying a ticket.

I squeezed into the small seat of a Braniff Airlines 707 Freedom Bird, painted cool, popsicle orange, on Da Nang airfield. Inside was hot as a pizza kitchen. The heat and cramped confines sparked a memory, niggling, as I thumbed through the in-flight magazine, *BI Pages*. Braniff International wanted to make a splash, so it hired Alexander Girard, graphic designer, to draw from a wild palette of colors for its planes—

lemon yellow, metallic purple and bright orange—spruce up its go-go image. *Pages* showed how Emilio Pucci had modernized and accessorized the sleek, Star Trek uniforms of their stewardesses. But let's not demean them—they were hostesses.

My narrow seat was unlike the spacious digs touted in the ads; eccentrics, Andy Warhol and Salvador Dali. Inside the boxcar they'd removed all first and business class seats and crammed in forty smaller ones. Outside, sweltering heat, the generator to kick-start the engines sat idle. Inside, no ice-cool air pumped through overhead jets. But within these muggy confines I sat suspended, physically buoyed like a hot air balloon at the prospect of leaving Vietnam. I cinched my seat belt tightly to stay tethered. Time melted like a Dali watch.

Outside the window, the hulk of a C-130 lay smoldering on the tarmac, mute testimony to the luck of NVA rocketeers. An oval frame, charred whale ribs lay crumpled on cement beach. Who in their right mind would sit in a bright orange bull's-eye on this tarmac? The garish plane taunted enemy spotters to vector 122 mm rockets from the rocket zone, two klicks north. Sitting exposed like this was counter-point to everything I'd ever learned about survival in Vietnam—camouflage, cover and concealment, never walk a trail, never sit in an orange plane in broad daylight. A muffled scream inside yelled, 'Get the *fuck out!*' I stuffed a pillow in its mouth.

I settled in and looked through the small portal. Heat waves rose from the liquid runway. The Truong Son Mountains shimmered in a sea of green. Warm, moist air rose from China Sea; topped treacherous Hai Van Pass with whipped cream.

The acrid stink, two hundred pairs of sweat stained khakis, stifled. Rivulets streaked my face. A Quartermaster captain beside me, flawless skin, movie-star profile, wore a National Defense Ribbon and Bolo Badge. A dumpy specialist filled the window seat and spilled into mine. My hand cast contained the overflow. Bracing my shoulder, I felt the reassuring press of a stiletto, tucked between the plaster cast and forearm. I cupped my hand as its tip pricked my palm. The cabin lights blinked as the generator sputtered to life. Hot, smothering air streamed through overhead jets and I struggled to breathe. A mixture of musk and JP-4 drifted down the isle, stung my nose.

A hostess, blond beehive, smiled and checked seat belts. She strolled gracefully in a plum dress, cut fashionably above her knees. A shiny gold dove pinned above her left breast, mimicked the rifle on my CIB. Her yellow print scarf draped loosely around a thin white neck. Four hundred eyes tracked pink Pucci pumps with green heels down the aisle. Across the aisle a private with sunburned face, white walls and flattop, flipped through *Pages* mindlessly but stopped to eyeball Pucci and his fashion III debut. He broke into a chant, "Poocee, Poocee, Poocee," as the hostess approached. As she bent to check a sergeant with shadowy beard, he made a peace sign.

"Make love not war," he said, grinning.

"I'm sure you will, sergeant," the hostess said. Her sweet, southern drawl disarmed.

"Where you from, sugar?"

"Love Field, Dallas."

"I'm sure you do." He chuckled softly, eyes scanning from head to pink pumps.

"Just keep it tight," the hostess said.

"Tight is right." His eyes flickered. "Like this little piece of fabric would save my ass if this here plane went up like a roman candle." He laughed and elbowed the sergeant next to him.

A pair of F-4 Phantoms rushed skyward; afterburners, blue tips of a welder's torch.

The plane inched forward at a snail's pace. I sat upright in my seat and clutched the in-flight magazine. Captain cool settled back in his isle seat. His tanned forearm pressed hard against my elbow. I locked my arm and shoulder in place and pretended to read, gave no quarter. He closed his eyes. I flipped the page. A raspy voice from behind yelled above the engines' whine. I turned.

" . . . got whacked is all I know!" Raspy said. His rough, eroded frame, wan complexion, and weepy elbow lesion confirmed boonie rat status.

"How?" asked his tawny sidekick.

"Crazy ass shit!" Raspy said. "I told Top, cousin or no, I was going to Sydney. Nothing I could do." A cluster of festering cuts adorned his arms.

"Hell, you could escort 'em home," cajoled his sidekick.

I glanced over my shoulder. Raspy's nametag read McMurry. He knitted his brow, removed a half sheet of yellow paper from his pocket. Pinholes lined fold marks of a dog-eared telegram. "KIA . . . deep in enemy territory," he laughed dismissively. "Wha-the-hells-zat mean?"

"Chu Pac Mountain. Don't get no deeper than that," chided Sidekick.

"Who they kiddin'?" Jet engines amped to a high-pitched whine.

"Operation Green Thunder, NVA blunder, we put a thousand gooks asunder!" Sidekick said.

Raspy crushed the paper and stuffed it in his pocket.

Sidekick sang to the tune of *Big Rock Candy Mountain*, "*We was buggered sore, like Charlie's whore, on Chu Pac misty mountain!*"

I stared forward at a two-page advertisement in *Pages*. A buxom blond in white pant suit smiled suggestively, spread across three airplane seats on her stomach, legs crossed. She plucked a single grape from a platter, offered by an unseen hostess. The caption read:

> *Ever since I made the centerfold of Playboy I fly Braniff.*
> *When you got it—flaunt it!*

"Me and Pete was going to Sydney," Raspy said. "Kick it hard."

"What the hell they tell you first day of basic training?" he said. "Don't volunteer! What'd he do? Signed up for Airborne, Special Forces."

My fingers touched the green beret folded crisply and tucked securely beneath my belt. I adjusted the ivory stiletto handle tucked in my cast while ignoring the insidious itch.

I flipped a couple more pages to another ad. A picture of a wide-mouth glass, rim covered with salt, filled with something like lemonade slush, garnished with succulent lime, graced the page. My mouth watered. The caption read:

Margarita is on our non-stop to Lima tonight.
Margarita is strong. Part Tequila
Margarita is sweet. Part fruit juice
Margarita is very good company on our non-stop to Lima.
Is it a Date?

I nodded; *it's a date,* though it'd have to wait until Sydney. How compassionate to serve up savory reminders on this long ass flight from hell.

The engines throttled up, bucked, as the pilot tested brakes. My stomach tightened. I bent forward and lifted my boots off the floor. The suave captain opened one eye and looked down.

"Tradition," I explained.

"Superstition." His patrician nose wrinkled as though he'd smelled a fart.

"Superstition?" I squinted at the leg captain. I set my boots down. Tell that to the burning bush, Sergeant First Class Ramon, Senior TAC NCO of 45th Company, Fort Benning, Georgia. Airborne!

I closed my eyes, heard Ramon's voice and pictured his final pep talk before my first airborne experience. There would be no quitters here. No refusals at the gate. At first it had a fatherly tone, the do's and don'ts of survival before senior prom. But as his fervor grew he plied us with that same intoxicating mixture of menace and machismo, *Death From Above*, an Airborne elixir to which we'd all been addicted.

We suited up at the field house in the Frying Pan—Lawson Air Field. So named because the flat land and surrounding hills resembled a skillet; blistering bacon, as men stood waiting in the Georgia sun.

As the jumpmaster inspected my chute, I surveyed the odd-looking planes, boxcars with twin-tails. My father had jumped the very same during WWII. Then a lieutenant assigned to the 508th Red Devils, he'd jumped into Holland. Now it was time to make my bones—or break some. I repeated his mantra, 'Any jump you walk away from is a good jump.'

SFC Ramon, front and center, strutted like a peacock. The barrel-chested Ramon wore a black cap with Master Blaster Wings and white T-shirt stenciled with name and rank. The crease in his fatigues could cut bread. Though Filipino, he sounded more like Ricky Ricardo. I strained to parse each word of the Caribbean crooner. His eyebrow twitched and biceps flexed as he made his pitch.

Scanning the formation, his black eyes fixed me with a steely gaze. "And just prior to takeoff each man *will elevate* his boots *perpendicular to* and *not less than* six inches off the floor." He charmed like a carnival barker. "This maneuver will enable your plane to rise *expeditiously* from this runway! Is that *clear!*"

We roared in unison, "*Clear* sergeant! *Airborne!*"

He delivered this command with such conviction that

failure to execute would cause inestimable damage.

I chuckled aloud. Of course there was no scientific basis for this, more tradition than anything. Yet when I climbed aboard that Fairchild C-119 Flying Boxcar, dubbed the *flying coffin*, and it rattled like a bucket of bolts ready to fly apart, I knew that Ramon had not misspoken. He knew that C-119's were underpowered and structurally so weak that periodically, times like this, tail-booms fell off in mid air. It had been so poorly designed an engineer proved mathematically it was impossible to get it off the ground, let alone fly. And yet it did.

I sat squeezed among a stick of thirteen airborne troopers on the port side of that C-119 boxcar with boots elevated perpendicular to and not less than six inches off the floor, engines revving as it tested brakes. I heard the murmurs of "*Hail Mary full of grace...*" the intermittent mumble of an "*Our Father...*" mixed with the giddy laughter of schoolboys jumping off a cliff into a quarry. One trooper stared ahead, wondered aloud, "*What have you gone and done?*"

The props of the Pratt & Whitney engines screamed so loud my eardrums almost burst. On takeoff the nose wheel shimmied like a dragster with a flat tire. The plane strained to lift, a gooney bird bouncing. Relief and alarm spread across our faces as we cleared the runway. A half-hour later I blew out the door at 1200 feet AGL. I looked up, suspended beneath the most beautiful white canopy I'd ever seen.

A loud fist-thump jolted the seat, shook me from reverie to reality. In the here and now, within this cramped space, the smell, heat and press of men came the awareness that this was just another boxcar and we were freight.

"Goddammit, Pete should be here!" Raspy said.

"Cool it!" Sidekick said. "They'll throw your ass off the plane!"

Breaks squealed as the plane came to a grinding halt. The bright orange bull's-eye sat idly at the end of the runway. I checked my watch, counted, figured we had a minute, two at most.

I glanced back at Raspy. The gaunt, red-faced soldier stared at his fist then at me with a 'What the fuck you lookin' at?' expression. I cocked an eyebrow.

"He's cool," Sidekick said. They wore Golden Dragon patches, 1/14 Infantry; motto, *Right of the Line*, curled beneath a slue-footed dragon. His forearm pinned the struggling pug.

"Everything OK?" the hostess asked. Bending down, she smiled disarmingly. Her scarf slid lightly across Raspy's face. He swatted at it, nodded absently and rubbed his swollen knuckles. The hostess winked and returned to her station.

The plane grew quiet. Captain snooze to the left of me, specialist to the right, Raspy behind, shattered and sundered, as there we sat, all sweaty, two hundred.

The dumpy specialist flipped soft-core pages of *Argosy*, men's magazine. A muscle-bound mercenary graced the cover. The bare-chested bandanna-wearing warrior, ammo belts draped, mowed down a hundred charging gooks one-handed with the M-60 machine gun. The brakes released and the wheels began to roll. The pucker factor climbed as I checked my watch, 67 seconds. The clueless captain relaxed.

As the plane accelerated every bowl and bump registered in the pit of my stomach I awaited that flash of light that would rip off the tail or wing. I gauged the ground speed and at the perfectly timed moment, lifted my feet perpendicular to and not less than six inches off the floor. Tradition or superstition—it had gotten me this far.

No one spoke or moved a muscle as the plane's nose tilted skyward and I felt that smooth carpet ride sensation and the cabin exploded with, *"Yeeaaassssss! Get sum! Sin loi motherfucker!"* The wheels retracted with a high-pitched squeal.

The private across the isle slapped his leg and hooted. The swarthy sergeant gave toothy grin. Then came a loud clunk as everyone lowered their feet in sync or maybe it was just the wheel doors snapping shut. As the plane banked sideways and headed out to the China Sea I looked down at a white plume of smoke rising from the runway.

"Holy cow!" the Specialist said. "That rocket could have blown us to kingdom come!" Absent the baggy khakis, he was a dead ringer for one of the seven dwarfs.

The cabin, except for Raspy, grew quiet. "Pete!" He pounded the armrest as my grip tightened around *Pages*. I looked down at the margarita advertisement—felt the promise of a cool glass sweating in my hand. I had an overpowering desire to bite into that succulent lime wedge and suck it dry. As I glanced at the hostess a crude notion replaced a fleeting fantasy.

I aimed a cool stream of air from the overhead jet at my face. Looking back, I checked Raspy's nametag again: McMurrry. Could he be talking about the McMurry assigned with me?

Pete, we called him Mac; more shadow than silhouette. His thin frame bent like a Bedouin as he crossed the sandy confines of our camp. His quick wit balanced an irregular stride. An infectious grin belied his penchant for mischief.

I recalled the *Top Secret* shithouse rumor weeks before. Mac and his hatchet platoon were part of a strike force tasked for a *Guns of Navarone* mission. *Argosy* hacks couldn't dream up this cockamamie scenario, a mix of pulp fiction and Greek tragedy.

Major "Speedy" Gaspard, S-3, ordered a task force of Special Commandos, SCU, to set down on top of the infamous Co Roc Mountain, located just across the Laotian border. The Japs had hollowed out a huge network of caves during occupation, WWII. NVA took ownership. Cannons rolled out from its caves on rails, fired and disappeared inside. During the siege of Khe Sanh, NVA spotters directed 122mm rockets and heavy artillery at the camp. The continuous pummeling of the impregnable fortress by B-52 bombers proved futile. Inside the honeycombed massif, worker bees buzzed safe and sound.

I pictured Mac, last time I saw him, standing in the door of a bubble-nosed H-34 helicopter lifting off the helipad. The chopper resembled a bullfrog; eyes recessed high above its round nose. Mac, cammied up, tiger-striped uniform and green cravat, sat in the door. He stared west toward Co Roc

Mountain, Sepon River coiling at its base.

I looked back at Raspy and shook my head. The McMurry I knew was either back at FOB-4 celebrating the mission or playing King of Co Roc Mountain. There was no way he was dead. *No fucking way* was I sitting in *his* seat on the way to Sydney in this orange boxcar with blond showgirls prancing in pinks and plums. But then Special Forces are practiced in the art of self-deception and plausible denial. Our trademark was twisting truth into a slipknot. We denied the obvious to attain the impossible.

The plane leveled off at cruising altitude. The drink cart came and went, dinner served and removed, lines formed at the lavatory and dwindled. Lotus-eaters slept. As hours passed the muffled roar of jet engines faded to a smooth vibration, for all but me. In addition to the maddening itch inside my cast, was an ice pick wedged in my middle ear. I swallowed hard, yawned, sucked down Coke, water, nothing relieved the pressure. I stood, squeezed past Captain Rip Van, stretched and glanced down at Raspy and Sidekick. They were locked in heated exchange. Raspy eyed the green beret tucked in my belt. His nostrils flared as I focused on the empty galley at the back of the plane. Comforted by the sight of Margarita, I rolled *Pages* and stuck it under my arm.

"SOG," Raspy said, nudged Sidekick; looking more like a mate off the Sloop John B.

A gauntlet of legs filled the isle. I swallowed and pounded my head like a swimmer and forced another yawn. *Did he say, SOG?* I pressed toward the back of the plane.

SOG—Studies and Observation Group, was cover for a clandestine unit whose specialty was sneak and peek, cross-border spy operations. Minimal Studies and little Observation; since it was virtually impossible to land a helicopter undetected anywhere near the Ho Chi Minh Road. By 1969 much of it had been paved. The mission was mostly a goddamn waste of brave warriors. I caught myself. McMurry was *not dead.* Missing, wounded perhaps—*not dead.*

I negotiated the phalanx of legs sprawled into the isle, tapping each one with the toe of my spit-shinned Cochran jump boot. The lavatory was cramped. Head bowed and shoulders scrunched as I drained the lily. A swirl of blue urine sucked down the metallic hole. I stared into the mirror suspicious of an alien in crinkled khakis, bristled blond, tapered cheekbones and rounded chin. Eyes peered from moon craters.

I slid the stiletto from my cast, pulled the plaster back, made room for its tapered blade; plunged it maddeningly against the itchy skin. Each stroke gave way to pleasurable relief but left its mark. Satisfied, I pushed it back into place and popped a pustule on my elbow. Salty semicircles had crystallized around the armpits. I yawned and something popped inside my head. Relieved, I grabbed *Pages* and stepped through the flimsy door.

Hostesses tended drink carts at the far end of the isle. I rested my head on the galley wall; listened to the muffled roar of engines, thirty thousand feet above the sea.

“Two words,” Raspy said. “Pete McMurry.”

I lifted my head slowly and took measure. His sturdy

frame had been rendered of all fat in the jungle caldron. His eyes flickered nervously; temples pulsed with each heave of the chest. Straightening, I pressed forward into the isle, flexed knees, shifting weight to the balls of my feet. I found the smooth handle of my stiletto with two fingers. *Mind zap. Whoa, slow down.*

I looked over Raspy's head and spotted the fat specialist making his way toward the piss tube. Raspy blocked the doors.

"Excuse me," the specialist said. Raspy ignored his plea and pulled the worn telegram from his pocket. "They think I'm stupid?"

"What makes you think that?"

" 'Lieutenant Pete McMurry died, deep in enemy territory,' " he read.

"You're blocking the door, sergeant," the specialist said.

"We work out of Chu Lai with the jarheads."

"Right of The Line!" I read the motto on his patch. "What the hell does that mean?"

"Civil war?" he said, "I don't rightly know."

He grimaced and pressed into me. I pivoted smoothly on my heel and in one movement parried his arm, spun him sideways and pinned him in the cramped passageway. I wedged my cast under his chin and pressed hard. The specialist ducked into the head and slammed the door with an audible click. The light flashed *Occupido* as sleeping men began to stir.

"I know you," he mocked.

"You don't know shit, sergeant."

"I seen you at Marble Mountain," Raspy said. "At the club."

His breath smelled vinegary.

"Never been there."

"I seen the skull with Green Beret, refrigerators, showers and that cement blockhouse with all them antennas," Raspy said. "All you prima donnas."

All true but the prima part. I'd never give him satisfaction. It was not surprising that Pete had bent the rules and brought Raspy into a *Top Secret* camp. He was trained in all manner of deception and misdirection and knew the risk if he was caught.

"Seventy-three days in the suck." Raspy gagged as I pressed his windpipe. "Drove Charlie across the river into Laos. Killed a hundred gooks." He twisted his body for leverage but I expanded my chest, locked my leg and pressed a knee into his groin.

The specialist opened the door. "Excuse me, sir."

Raspy squinted and stared at the silver bar and crossed rifles on my lapel. "Sir?"

"Sergeant?"

"All I seen was Green Beret." Raspy shifted his eyes toward the specialist. "Get the fuck outta here," he growled. A grizzled NCO with 101st Screaming Eagle patch looked around from his seat. I shook my head.

"Need any help, sir?" the specialist asked. He hiked his baggy pants.

"Does it look like it, dumb ass?" Raspy said. The specialist retreated down the isle and I caught sight of the blonde hostess at the far end. A couple of heads swiveled; eyed the commotion.

"What about this?" He raised the telegram.

"Charlie gets pushed across the river. Maybe somebody's got to find him."

"You mean Pete?"

"Did I say that?" Plausible denial is an art form.

"Why?" Raspy asked. "*Why?*"

I relaxed my grip. I'd been schooled in the art of spin, nothing into something and vice versa. "Maybe it was just his nature," I said. "Ever hear about *The Scorpion and the Frog*?"

I told a quick story, how the scorpion asked a frog for a ride across a river on his back. Halfway across the scorpion stung him. 'Why?' asked frog in disbelief, for now they both would surly die. 'It's just my nature,' said scorpion.

"What the fuck that got to do with anything?"

I lifted my cast from under his chin and pointed to the motto on his patch, *Right of the Line*. "Well, maybe Pete worked, *Left of the Line*."

It took a minute. Raspy's dark eyebrows arched and he nodded. "Just his nature," he said. "Never thought of it that way."

"You have your traditions and we have ours," I said. Raspy picked up the crumpled magazine and stared at Margarita.

"I'm hoping she does the trick when we get to Sydney," I said.

Raspy licked his cracked lips and tucked in rumpled shirt. "Yes, sir," he said, "Me too." He straightened his shoulders and handed it back. "But what if it doesn't?"

"Then it won't," I said.

Raspy walked back as the drink cart made its slow return and the blond hostess stooped to serve.

I stepped back into the galley, pulled the stiletto from my cast and studied the double-edged blade and curved guard. I pricked my finger with pointy-tip then pulled the plaster away and ran the blade up and down until it turned red; wiped it clean on the magazine and tucked it away. I leaned forward and rested my head on the cast.

Something touched my shoulder and I swung my elbow around but managed to stop just short of a lovely face.

"Whoa, lieutenant! You're wound pretty tight," the hostess said.

"Tight is right," I said.

"Not really." She smiled and adjusted her silk scarf, removed the magazine from my hand and glanced at Margarita. "Everything okay?"

"Nothing she won't cure," I said. How many, I wondered, would it take to erase all memory? I studied the smiling hostess. Another inch and that sleek beautiful nose would have been smashed.

"Maybe you should take the empty crew seat in the corner, lieutenant," she said. "Where I can keep an eye on you."

"Likewise, I'm sure." I sunk into the thickly padded seat, twice the size of mine and settled in. Maybe this was what Alexander Girard had in mind. I looked at *Pages* and Margarita, pictured Pete and the odds of my landing in that seat. I thought about my first ride into combat and my father's before me. Was I a scorpion or frog? Did I have a choice or did my double helix demand all this? Was it *my nature*, gift or curse?

SOG men flew across the Sepon River. Some were frogs, some scorpions, to each his own. But if there was one thing I was sure of—the frog was no victim. Each had suspicions about the scorpion's nature but suspended logic and intuition for the artful lie. Turns out, a trusty frog is a dead frog.

Comfort is contagious. I fell into a heavy sleep. Something shook me and I woke with a start. The blond hostess stepped back as she extended a tray with the same wide-mouthed glass pictured in the ad. The rim was covered with salt, the glass chocked full of ice, filled with something like lemonade. I compared the two. It wasn't garnished with a lime wedge, had no liquor, but it sparkled with promise.

"Love Field." I nodded, grateful for her effort.

"Touchdown in twenty."

"Love Margarita," I said.

"Sorry she's not the real thing."

"Where would I get that?"

"Where else? The Texas Tavern, Kings Cross."

"To the real thing." I toasted. As I sipped the drink my desires shifted to the need for something more than Margarita to quench my thirst. Love Field nodded and began her checklist for landing; walked up the isle for a final trash run.

I walked back to my seat and looked down at Captain Rip Van; eyed the Quartermaster insignia, absent Airborne Wings, CIB. His coiffed hair, impeccable skin and manicured nails relayed an unmistakable air of destiny, thirty years pushing paper toward a star. Yet here we sat in the same boxcar.

As the hostess neared with her half-filled bag I wanted to say something to the paper-shuffling captain about traditions; how repetitive acts trigger memories. It doesn't matter whether they are born of fact or fiction, truth or superstition—it's all the same. Raising my feet perpendicular to and not less than six inches off the floor allowed me to concentrate on the things I could control and forget about things I couldn't. A lifer should understand traditions are born of feelings imprinted deep in our bones; conscious deeds bonded to memory, past and future fused into one present wordless moment of clarity. Traditions allow us to look out the door of a Flying Boxcar into chaos and *know* we can survive the jump.

Love Field extended her trash bag, "Five minutes, lieutenant." I winked, dropped the magazine into the bag, but not my fantasy. I took a seat.

EPILOGUE

It wasn't until I returned to FOB-4 Marble Mountain after R&R, I received confirmation Lieutenant Pete McMurry had been killed on Co Roc. The Air Force bombed it around the clock before the assault. The 500 pounders did little more than stir the nest. It was a kind of twisted irony that he was killed by the frog he'd ridden across the Sepon River. A Vietnamese pilot misjudged final approach and careened into the LZ; hit so hard that it pitched sideways toward McMurry who stood nearby. A rotor clipped his head, killed him instantly. The task force was extracted with seven wounded and three dead.

Years later as I wandered through an exhibition of Rodin, I happened upon the statue of *Walking Man*. I was struck by the sculpture's exquisite detail and physicality of its muscular legs and torso. Something struck me about how he'd captured motion. The headless form only served to accentuate his powerful stride. Marveling the craftsmanship, the form sparked a vague memory. The forward tilt of *Walking Man* reminded me of Lieutenant Pete McMurry. Its unique form conveyed the very essence of Pete; his drive and sense of perpetual motion. To this day, I see him pitched forward—braced against the swirl, taking his last, long eternal stride.

COLOR ME RED

I sat buckled in the hold of a C7-A Caribou flying to Mai Loc, near the Laotian boarder, 1968. I'm wedged against boxes of LuRP and C-rations, ammo cans, and a tightly tethered water buffalo with brass nose ring. The camouflaged bush plane smelled of dung and ammonia, chicken feathers floated. The Caribou, designed for short take off and landings, drifted, dropped and rose again in the Asian thermals, as the powerful flanks of the buffalo edged ever close. The Pratt & Whitney engines strained as the plane lifted and fell. It rattled and rolled as I glanced upstairs into the cockpit. The co-pilot knitted his brow and studied his landing checklist. I strained to see out the port window as the din and discord of hydraulics squealed, flaps lowered, engines slowed, and wheels dropped. The tailgate folded down, exposing a vast checkerboard of emerald paddies, rolling hills and jungle. Intrigued, I stood, removed my web gear and stepped perilously close to the ramp's edge. Allured by the vivid splash of colors I slipped my hand through a nylon handhold and peered down. The plane bucked violently. My tethered hand felt a vicious tug, feet lifted and torso stretched into the slipstream, bull rider hung on an eight second ride. My arm shook violently, hand tore loose and I tumbled through space until I arched my back and spread my arms into a stable free fall position. Amazed to be alive, every nerve in my body fired as I plunged toward a bright red strip of clay surrounded by jungle. I felt for my ripcord handle and realized I had no chute, . . . everything went red. I awoke, took a deep gulp of air and sat up in bed. "Same dream?" said a soft voice. I felt the soothing touch of a hand rub my back.

"Yeah," I said. "Same dream. Go back to sleep."

"It's alright," she hushed.

"Yeah. Just a dream, nobody gets hurt."

I sat in the small bullpen at Harrison Realty. Directly behind me, Big Lynn's office, a large square window with Venetian blinds drawn. From behind this curtain his voice boomed like the Wizard.

Big Lynn fought with the 504th Airborne Regiment in Italy, World War II. "We were in the mountains—on line, in winter for sixty-six days." He closed his left eye as if sighting a rifle. "The Germans called us *Devils in Baggy Pants.*" Big Lynn's chest expanded, spine stiffened, when he recalled his war.

The phone rang as I read the *Wall Street Journal,* a habit developed from my brief but unspectacular career with Merrill Lynch, Pierce, Fenner and Dildo. I cooled, starched collar open, from an early morning workout at Nautilus Center. I'd abandoned the free weights of my youth for precision weight training.

As I reached for the phone Colleen sashayed into the office. Her spiked heals left red bird tracks the length of the narrow room. She was Big Lynn's most productive real estate agent. Her curvaceous credentials meant she knew how to sell it. She ignored me and headed to the back room to make coffee.

"Harrison Realty." I smiled into the phone. Zig Ziglar, a combination of motivational speaker and zealot, said that customers could hear the smile in your voice. The wall clock read 8:28—early for Colleen.

"This is Major Evans," the officious voice said. "I'm a career councilor at OPPERCEN, in St. Louis. Your commission is about to expire."

"Send the paper work when it's over." I laughed dismissively. I didn't recognize the voice and it was way too early for a staff officer to be up, let alone cold calling. Anyway, OPPERCEN, whatever the hell that was, didn't have my address, where I worked or what I did for a living. How could they?

"Is there any way that you would stay in the reserve?" he asked.

"How'd you get this number?" I strained for a clue. "That you Don?" Maybe it was my old friend who served with the 173rd Airborne in Vietnam. He was prone to play prankster. He'd stuffed a dead seagull in the grill of my car after I hid one under his seat.

"We need a few good men," he said.

"Tried the marines?" I remembered how jarheads had almost gotten me killed a couple of times, but never returned the favor. "Who put you up to this?"

"What's your current home address?"

"Street Without Joy," I said. I'd just finished Bernard Fall's book, *Hell In a Very Small Place: The Battle of Dien Bien Phu*, written 1966, the year I enlisted in the army. It was a case study on how the French lost Vietnam in 1954 and a blueprint for our disaster.

"I understand your anger," he said. "I talk with a lot of officers."

I recognized technique. Show empathy–gain trust and ask for the order. "Is this a fucking joke?"

As I listened to the mystery voice Big Lynn pulled into the parking lot and stepped from his brand spanking new camper with pop-up roof, slept six, with all the accouterments of home. The tires were freshly coated with clay, running boards and mud flaps spattered.

"Any way you'd stay in the reserve?"

"There is *no* fucking way," I said. Sweat dripped. I lifted a towel from my gym bag and wiped. "Are we clear?"

"You had good assignments, Special Forces, MACV SOG, good OER's, line and staff duty."

"Good for whom?" I rubbed my scarred little finger when I grew agitated. It was numb and curved like a scimitar. "What don't you understand about *no*?" Silence.

"Who'd you serve with in Nam?" I asked.

"1st Infantry."

"A big red one."

"No sacrifice too great."

"For the living or dead?"

Big Lynn nodded as he entered, thin hair, broad shoulders, tweed coat and striped tie. He headed straight for the back room. I swiveled in my chair and looked away pretending to gaze at framed and forlorn, General Robert E. Lee on Traveler, *Surrender at Appomattox*.

"I reviewed your records," said Evans.

I clamped my jaw and pressed my lips to the phone. "*Review this!*" My words hissed through locked teeth. "I ain't *fucking* interested!" The anger boiling up surprised me.

"Maybe you can help us get it right next time," he said.

"There won't be a *next time*!"

"How does that go? 'Wars and rumors of war—but the end is not yet,'" he said.

"Well I've beaten my bayonet into a time-share."

"What about those hard won memories?" he asked.

"Here's one, I read in the *Journal* where Uncle Sam thinned the ranks, RIF'd officers with combat experience for the 'convenience of the army' and now you need weekend warriors to take up the slack?"

"Needs change in every business," he said. "But there are benefits."

"Weekend drills, two weeks active duty and then it's 'All the way with LBJ?'" I asked. "What about the next Texas tough guy looking to play sheriff?"

"If I found you a slot in a Special Forces unit would you stay in?"

"Special Forces?" My throat cleared. Something shifted slightly but I didn't take the bait. I wiped my face with my shirtsleeve and squinted at Lee, something I'd never noticed—clay spattered boots.

"I'll see what I can do, captain." His voice soothed. I knew an assumptive close when I heard one. It was right off the training tape, *No Doze—How To Close*. I didn't expect that from a major. My scalp was on fire.

"*No!* Not *now*, not *fucking ever!*" I slammed the phone. My armpits were dark moons. I was anti-war, anti-army, anti-Nixon, anti-Republican and we were just coming out of a recession. I had a family to feed and had no intention of going into the reserve.

I walked to the rear of the office. Colleen stood with her back towards me at the coffee maker. Big Lynn stood close behind. His hands slid down and away from her hips. He turned as I entered the room. Colleen straightened her crumpled collar, lifted it above her exposed neck and walked into the main office.

"Who was on the phone?" Big Lynn asked. He squinted with one eye.

"Some major from St. Louis."

"You know I don't abide that kind of talk, no matter how despicable the character," he said. His elegant drawl rankled.

"They want me back in the army."

"People in hell want ice water," he said, feet spread, knees locked, drill instructor precision. "Expect another war if the Trilateral Commission continues to foment."

My eyes glazed over and I returned to my chair. I tuned out the rant about the Trilateral Commission and Bilderbergers. Even now he was convinced Dr. Martin Luther King was a communist. His unchecked resentments and conspiracies had devoured him and everything around him, maybe even me.

Colleen sat erect as a swan at her desk. Just above her up-turned collar was a yellowish bruise. Not long married, I ignored the implications. I prided myself on the purity of my vows. But the major's phone call had sparked some latent thirst, ignored or denied; tantamount to a dry alcoholic watching a beer commercial.

I looked down at my daily action planner. 'If you don't have daily objectives, you can't qualify as a dreamer.' That's what Zig Ziglar said in *See You At The Top*. I knew about objectives. Infantry officers were imprinted with regimen, discipline and prioritization. Is that what the major meant by '*getting it right*?' Did I have to believe in perpetual war or suspend disbelief?

Two words, Special Forces, threatened to pierce a carefully constructed façade of normalcy. I'd worked hard to rebuild my identity in the intervening years, but mostly; remembered to forget. Too much remembering can kill you. I replayed the phone call and prided myself on my forceful and unequivocal 'fuck you' response. I'd sent a clear and convincing message that shored up my rock solid resolve.

I dug through the bottom drawer of my desk and found, *Principles of Sun Tsu*. I'd studied the book while working for Mother Merrill. My branch manager, a jarhead reservist, used Principles to inspire a new class of financial warriors. Turns out, the client was the enemy, so I surrendered.

I flipped through the pages to an underlined passage: '*Victorious warriors win first and then go to war—while defeated warriors go to war first and then seek to win.*' The Joint Chief's never imagined a tiny, third world country like Vietnam would slay Goliath and route the Philistines. I'd learned greater appreciation for the vanquished.

Big Lynn stopped beside my desk. "Colleen and I are going to preview some properties," he said. "We'll be back in a couple hours."

"Which ones?" I asked.

"We'll have a sit down when I get back." Colleen strutted out the door, left a second set of bird prints. Big Lynn's brogans tracked behind.

Two months later the dust had settled and I had all but forgotten about the phone call. I hadn't mentioned anything to my wife, Elizabeth. It was the ides of March and I'd moved on. The phone rang and as I drew the receiver close, a waggish tune filled my ear.

"*You're in the army now, you're not behind a plow, . . .*"

"Who is this?"

"Major Evans, from OP-PER-CEN. Remember?"

"We've had this discussion," I said.

"I pulled some strings—found you a slot in a Special Forces company."

"I appreciate your persistence, but I'm not interested!" But something between nausea and bliss informed my disposition.

"Look captain, I forwarded your 201-File to Company B, 11th Special Forces, Richmond. They're expecting you for a MUTA-5 drill next weekend."

"Are you deaf?" I asked.

"You know how hard it is to get an A-Team commander slot?

"And you're doing this because?"

"The company has a jump laid on this weekend."

"As tempting as that is . . ."

"They just returned from England, training with the SAS."

"I've got commitments."

"You'll get more training in the reserve than you did in the regular army."

"For what?"

"Maybe I was wrong, this isn't for you," the major said. "People change, lose their edge."

"Like you."

"This isn't about me," he said. "It's what you bring to the party, your experience. Think about how you could impact unit readiness. Now, 'stand in the door!'"

"Like I said."

"Green light, captain."

"Not so fast."

"Well that's a start."

"No chance."

"One chance," he said. "At some unfinished business."

"All done," I said.

"You sure about that?" he asked. "Take this down."

"Anything to make you stop." I wrote down Michelli Reserve Center.

"Airborne!" The phone clicked. He was gone, silence raged in my ear. I crumpled the paper and trashed it.

She found me rummaging through mildewed boxes in the cellar after I'd tucked the kids in bed and told a story. The writing on the boxes, stacked along the damp wall, was faded and unreadable. I tore through the boxes with a kind of frantic urgency. A sour smell of mold filled the dank basement. A bulwark of cinderblocks and sand reinforced the crumbling foundation.

"It's late," Elizabeth said. The overhead light reflected off coppery hair. Her angular frame and muscular legs were outlined beneath a flimsy negligee.

"Where're my jungle boots and camouflage fatigues?" I tore open soggy cardboard flaps.

"Going hunting?"

"I've been assigned to a reserve Special Forces Company."

"What?"

"I report this weekend." I ripped open another box.

"What are you talking about?" she said. "You had your fill of all that!"

"I'm just going back to check it out." I pulled out a crumpled set of jungle boots, covered with a mossy sheen.

"What about work—the kids?" Her eyes flashed.

"It's just one weekend," I said. I swiped the mold from a boot and pulled the dry-rotted lace. It snapped.

"Maybe that's an omen," she said.

"It's the reserves, for God's sake," I said. "I'm just checking it out!"

"What does that mean?"

"It's just one weekend a month."

"So you've already made up your mind?"

"Maybe I can train some men to . . ."

"Survive?" she asked. "Really? When were you going to tell me?"

"I can't explain," I said. "They called; offered me a slot."

"You've got a slot," she said. "Family slot. Right here!"

"You know how hard it is to get an A-Team?"

"Life's a bitch."

"I know."

She shrugged and retreated in silence.

"I'm just checking it out," I yelled after. "Nobody gets hurt!"

Buckled in the hold of a C7-A Caribou I stared across the floor at another A-Team rigged for a combat jump; rucksacks and rifles. Ashen faces and drool betrayed steely constitutions. An hour into the flight the plane dropped precipitously into a roller coaster plunge and my stomach floated in zero gravity. I looked down the line at the newly assigned A-Team as the plane reversed its plunge, lifted violently. My stomach compressed into a ball and pressed hard to exit my ass. I gripped the seat webbing over my shoulder with one hand and the aluminum bar with the other. Each vicious sheer and upward reversal torqued the aluminum frame as wing grommets groaned and stomachs sloshed.

A gaunt, green sergeant across the aisle looked up, Adam's apple bobbing. He swiped drool from his mouth. His pallid face and wondering eyes conveyed a desperate need to exit. Jumpers covered mouths with both hands, struggling not to breach. One man blows, we all go.

The gangly co-pilot in baggy flight suit gripped the ladder, climbed slowly from the cockpit. He sat and scooted along the floor, hand over mouth; cheeks stretched like a trumpeter. He gripped the anchor line cable stretching from bulkhead to floor at the rear of the plane. He floated momentarily then slammed violently. A brown stream shot from his mouth.

The air smelled of rotten eggs and Limburger. The pod breached, blowholes spouting. I gagged and swallowed an acidy lump, determined not to puke.

The red light blinked on and the jumpmaster yelled "Stand up!" The tailgate folded down, exposing a checkerboard of black and gray. Barren trees brushed the gunmetal sky. The steady blast of cold air numbed the fingers and froze cheeks.

The jumpmaster shouted "One minute!" I careened against the bulkhead slipping on slick viscous as the plane rose and dropped. I gripped the nylon netting with the right hand and the static line in the left. A jumper slipped and crashed to the floor. I bent knees and spread legs, intent on ending this nightmare.

The plane bucked and shimmied on the final approach. Green light lit to a dissonant chorus of gratitude and groans. I reached the edge of the ramp and bunny hopped; awaited the tug of a smooth opening. Instead I felt a savage jerk on my arm and my body unfurled like a banner. My head snapped back and something ripped. I reached for the toggles of the MC-1-1 but one arm hung limp along my side. I pulled the other toggle and my chute spun like a top. I drifted toward electrical lines strung between lattice steel transmission towers. I blinked hard and tried to wake. As my chute spun and I dropped ever close to the power lines the stark realization came that I was drifting, completely out of control. I listened for her soft voice, 'Same dream?' and the soothing rub of her hand on my back. Everything went red.

CHALLENGING DISASTER

> You know you have people down here making decisions who've never even flown an airplane before.
>
> Michael J. Smith, Astronaut
> January 28, 1986

> And all this science I don't understand, it's just my job five days a week.
>
> *Rocket Man,* Elton John

January 28, 1986

I penned evaluation reports, EERs for my A-Team, reviewed next month's training schedule, lesson plans, IG inspection prep, requisitions for parachutes and Q-school for the newly assigned. The army doesn't march on its stomach, it low crawls on paperwork.

I pushed the stack aside and downed eggs, grits and biscuits in the Dixie Diner. The high-pitched whistle of the Lionel train circled the room and passed overhead. Small Os puffed from the engine's smoke stack. A gust of cold air swept the isle as the front door opened. A line of bubba's sat at the counter spooning grits and red-eye gravy. It felt good to be sequestered in the back booth.

Next came business, a Private Placement Memorandum (PPM) Stock Offering for Henderson & Fenwick, "hereafter known as H&F."

THE SHARES OFFERED HEREBY ARE HIGHLY SPECULATIVE, AND INVESTMENT IN THESE SHARES INVOLVES A HIGH DEGREE OF RISK (SEE "RISK FACTORS")

Reviewing the PPM filled me with a fleeting sense of satisfaction, challenge and exhilaration. Financial transactions registered low on my risk meter, which if not broken, had been badly damaged. Vietnam had expanded my tolerance for risk far beyond the normal range. Just how far? I hadn't a clue. Absolute risk or as close as I could get to it in civilian life was deferred to weekend drills in the Special Forces Reserve. I was an adrenaline junkie and got my fix with fly-aways; night drops in Panama, leaping from Mark-IV SOC boats into the shark-infested Caribbean.

Other than trading puts and calls on the CBOE, Chicago Board of Options Exchange, this was the first investment that provided the kick I needed to feel alive; though far less intoxicating than flying nap of the earth in a C-130 Blackbird out of Hurlburt Field; rigged and ready for a night jump. This private placement had financial elements of chance that far exceeded its risk ratio. But it was still a two-dollar fix for a hundred-dollar habit.

As one of the Young Turks, a loose confederation of branch managers and hotshot brokers, we conspired to take the high ground; dislodge Fenwick as president and grow the company. Subscription completed, the die had been cast. Fenwick would soon be voted out as president. Today's meeting, I guessed, was a lame attempt at prolonging the inevitable.

I flagged Bea and pointed at my cup. Thin as a twig, hair piled high, silver bracelets dangled from her wrist. My cup brimmed over as she preened in the mirror then scooped up the empty plate. I put away the document and scanned the *Times Dispatch.*

"You stay here much longer and Charlie's going to charge you rent," said Bea. I stifled a yawn. "No sleep again last night?" She leaned forward and brushed my shoulder, rubbernecked the headline:

Challenger Attempts Launch Again Today
Local Schools Set to Watch Christa McAuliffe
First Teacher in Space

She crooned in my ear. "*She packed my bags last night preflight. Zero hour, nine a.m.*" Glittery nails slid the ticket across the table.

"Don't you just luvvvv Elton John?"

"Got the time?" I asked.

"You got the money honey, I got the time," she said. "Where's your watch? An impo-tent man like you needs a watch."

"Haven't worn jewelry since Vietnam."

"'*Til touchdown brings me round again to find,*'" she sang. "No weddin' ring neither." She hoisted a Heinz ketchup bottle and sang into the mic, "*I'm not the man they think I am at home.*"

"Who is?"

"*Rocket Ma-aaan.*" She bent forward in a crouch. "I miss the earth so much I miss my wyyyiiife." She glanced at her Wonder Woman watch, "Zero hour, eight a.m."

"Running late." I left a tip and picked up the tab.

"Generous." She straightened my paisley tie.

"Don't give up your day job."

I slid the bill across the counter to the cashier and flipped a coin, "Double or nothing?"

"Do I look like a big shot investment banker?" he asked, ringing the register. "A bird in the hand, I always say."

"Where will that get you?" I smiled and hustled out.

"It keeps the doors open." He yelled after.

Bea amped her vocals as the door slammed. "*And I think it's going to be a long, long time.*"

I didn't care if F.W. showed for the meeting or not. I was focused; felt driven by some inexplicable need to watch the shuttle launch, zero hour, nine a.m.

I stepped from the heart of Dixie into a frigid blast of arctic air. The raw wind chafed. I looked down Bank Street toward the Siege Museum. The morning sun lit the imposing Greek revival architecture, four white columns and Doric edifice.

I ignored the flashing lights, ineluctably yellow, in the middle of the street. A-frame barricades warned of fallen brick and block; fractured facades, toppled and smashed during last night's gale. I scanned unseen, a long line of empty buildings; drunkards tilting shoulder to shoulder. As I reached my car I felt the crunch and crackle of glass beneath my feet. I hauled the portable TV to my office door.

The three storied Farmer's Bank sported red brick and green shutters. My skeleton key rattled the lock. The second floor, converted to elegant offices, was decorated with period antiques. A sign read:

H&F, Members New York Stock Exchange

F.W. Henderson, second-generation silver spoon, had been born on third base, but believed he'd hit a triple. He was acting president, but he'd never really auditioned for the part. He'd been father's understudy but a failure in the role. He and sister Sarah were principal stockholders. Capital requirements imposed by the SEC meant H&F had to raise money by selling stock. The Young Turks, knowledgeable insiders, formed an alliance and conspired to retire the confederate dunce.

I stepped into a long hallway. Pitted stairs and mahogany balustrade ascended at the far end of the foyer. It was dark and drafty as a French prison. An eighteenth century hanging, *The Fox Hunt*, covered the wall. I hauled the TV to the second floor mezzanine. The landing opened to a broker's bullpen and separate but adjoining offices for my secretary and me.

An alabaster bust of Odysseus sporting a green beret stared vacantly from the fireplace mantel. A drawing of me bandaged like a mummy and strapped on cargo pallet, leaned against the large mirror. A row of army plaques, statues, awards and decorations filled the mantle. At the far end, Green Berets rigged for a water jump, squinted into the lens. The framed article:

President Reagan Attends 200th Anniversary of Yorktown
Special Forces Provide Airborne Excursion

I lifted a pillow and afghan blanket from the King Edward couch where I'd slept the night before. I surveyed the office, stepped into the bullpen. Two rows of desks were littered with holding books and buy/sell tickets. Cigarettes floated in coffee cups, ashtrays brimmed. Cursors winked mindlessly, blank screens of quote machines.

Stockbrokers evolved by natural selection and were, in some respects, mere vestiges of their cousins, annelids. Bloodsuckers by design, could drain the economic life out of a customer in a New York second. SEC 202: *Know Your Customer Rule,* was in short the purview of prostitutes, laws writ large with precise ambiguity.

I tucked the pillow and blanket under the sink. Mr. Coffee gurgled and spit as I gazed upon the Appomattox River, history laid bare. On its banks, Peter Jones Trading Station, where Indians parked canoes and traded sacred smoke for trinkets.

The aroma of Old Mansion wafted from my cup as I moved the TV to my credenza. Tin foil flags adjusted nicely on the rabbit ears and I muted the sound. Watching television during work felt strange, but the anticipation of flight produced a kind of euphoric recall.

As the shuttle vented steady streams on the launch pad, high school memories stirred, John Glenn's first orbit. I played hooky whenever NASA launched. I missed the moon landing when in Vietnam. The only lift off I was worried about that day was the UH-1D chopper snatching us up on a hot LZ. All systems were a go as me and my team ran for our lives in the Ashau Valley. Neil Armstrong must have had the same exhilarating feeling about the time he stepped on the moon. While he took one small step for man, I took one giant leap for my kind, into a hovering chopper. The pilot pulled collective and plucked us, *deus ex machine*; in a hail of gunfire. It was funny how indiscriminant memories, events, men, dead and alive, popped into my brain like that. One minute I could be sitting in my chair the next whizzed off to a jungle firefight. Seemed like it happened more and more often.

I checked my calendar, sipped coffee and finished team EERs. I watched the pre-launch show and turned on the Quotron, news and quotes. The dark screen flickered, iridescent, firefly green.

The Challenger sat poised for take off. Its wing-swept body strapped to an orange external tank, bracketed by two solid rocket boosters, SRBs. They'd fire for eight and a half minutes and tumble back to earth. I turned up the sound.

"During the night a stiff north wind blew across the external tanks. An eye wash fountain left on, covered the solid rocket boosters with a sheet of ice," the announcer said. A service team melted the ice with steam hoses. A notice scrolled across the screen *FLIGHT DELAYED.*

The downstairs door slammed. One by one four stockbrokers plodded past my door, casualties of a Duck's

Unlimited after-party.

"Did I miss the meeting?" I asked.

Elsa, tall, broad-shouldered Slav, marched into her office.

"Wind about blew me over," she said. She shook her head and dropped an armload of mail.

"What gives?" I stepped into our dividing doorway. Her tussled red hair fell lightly across the pale skin of her neck. In the soft light she could have been Olga, Munch's mistress. Her large hand wielded a letter opener with harsh precision.

"I'm expecting F.W. this morning," I said.

"Mr. Henderson?" She frowned. "Why didn't you say?" She looked absently toward the mezzanine, gears turning behind her eyes.

"He called last night," I said. "Something about an Executive Committee meeting over the weekend.

"He's never been here."

"Just routine."

"Aren't you on that committee?" she asked.

"Weekend drill." I said.

"Another jump from a perfectly good plane?" She shook her head.

"Airborne."

"You OK?"

"Just running down the road trying to loosen my load," I said.

"Is that a song?" she asked. "I'd worry more about your bones."

"Bring F.W. a cup of coffee when he comes in."

"I'm not a waitress."

"We've been through this. It's a courtesy we extend to our clients."

"So now he's a client?"

"He's my . . . " I checked myself. I didn't consider him my boss. He was the titular head of a failing brokerage company, the profligate son who'd run his financial ship aground. "You can handle it. And while I think of it, check the numbers on the Jameson portfolio. Make sure quarterly dividends are posted," I said. "And here's next month's training schedule, requisitions and some evaluations to type."

"Yes, drill sergeant." She saluted awkwardly. "Any chance of that raise?"

"About the same as that shuttle lifting off," I said, "And yes, sir will do just fine."

F.W. parked his 1967 pale green, Pallas Citroen in front of the Farmer's Bank in a NO PARKING/BUSES ONLY/TOW ZONE. It reminded me of another Citroen, blown upside down on Highway 1 outside Da Nang, wheels spinning lazily. I blinked and shook my head, annoyed by the intrusion. Life was humming right along with work and I had reserves as a release valve. There were family issues but as far as business went I was strapped in at the controls, ready for lift off.

F.W. was tall with gaunt English features and a thin black comb-over. A neighbor kid shot his eye out with a BB gun. His slumping posture and rounded shoulders were exacerbated by head tilt. His dead eye reminded me of a Nung striker who stepped on a mine, exploded in front of me. Truth was I couldn't remember what he looked like, just laying on my back, trying to breathe, head ringing and bleeding from the ears. It felt like a heart punch. Sergeant Dixon screaming soundlessly, "You all right? You all right?" His lips moved. No words sounded.

F.W. arrived after the second Challenger delay, mounted the stairs and tapped lightly on the doorframe. His West End pedigree sported an English tweed jacket, black turtleneck sweater, dandruff and brown oxfords, scuffed from heel to toe, no socks or belt. I swiveled in my chair as I finished a phone call.

"Yes, Brandon, full presentation, three o'clock Wednesday." I hung up.

"H-R Director from Brown & Williamson," I said. "They're closing down the factory. Four thousand jobs gone." I scribbled a note on my calendar. "It's taken me two years to get in the door."

"Big tobacco is dead," F.W. said. He crossed the room and extended limp, tobacco-stained fingers. I looked into his eyes. His good eye was as vacuous as the glass one. He walked toward the fireplace and inspected the mantel. I retrieved a Kleenex and wiped my hand.

"The local gendarmes won't ticket my car will they?" F.W. asked.

"Good luck has its storms."

"What's with the barricade?"

"High winds, old buildings."

He stared at a picture on the mantle, me standing at attention in front of a company formation. "Officer and gentleman," he said.

"Award ceremony."

"Green Beret? I was 4F, didn't believe in that war."

"War's an article of faith."

"Intelligence nets, dark arts, double agents and plausible denial."

"The key word is plausible."

"I read *The Green Beret.*"

"You know that's fiction."

"It's like this business; lies fly and truth arrives on a stretcher," he said. "How'd that song go . . . *fearless men who jump and die*?"

F.W. sat on a leather couch, crossed his gangly legs and exposed the hole in his sole. He examined the Queen Anne coffee table and stroked its cabriole legs. "Excellent reproduction."

"It's period," I said. "The Historical Foundation loaned it to us."

Elsa brought coffee on a silver tray. F.W. nodded as I introduced her.

"Close both doors," I said.

"Yes, sir," said Elsa. Frowning, she raised her hand slightly in salute.

"First time I've seen the operation," said F.W. "Now remind me . . . how long we been here?" He tapped his temple.

"Five years," I said. "I got back in the business in 1981 after reading, *The Death of Equities* in *BusinessWeek.*"

"Remarkable space," he said, scanning the high ceilings

and Italian marble fireplace. F.W. slid his hand inside his coat and removed a pack of Pall Mall.

"You mind?" he said, without looking up.

"My mother smoked Pall Mall," I said. F.W. searched the pack for the last cigarette.

"Ashtray?" He fingered the pack, waved it like a red flag.

"Died of emphysema," I said. There was no urge to accommodate.

"Sorry, must have missed that," he said, coughing. The secondary smoke was less an affront than the logo on the red pack. The inscription: *Per aspera ad astra*, "through hardships to the stars." F.W. lit the cigarette, crumpled the empty pack, tilted his head back and exhaled a perfect O like the mysterious woman that once graced the billboard on Jeff Davis Highway.

It was with great excitement and anticipation, as a child, that I prepared for a glimpse of her. I had only seconds to study her face as we passed the Jeff Davis billboard on the way to Richmond; just seconds to study her rounded red-lips, blond hair and expressive eyes. I pressed hard against the window to see her inscrutable smile and perfect Os of smoke, big as a bike wheel, pumping effortlessly through white teeth. Whatever the hour, day or night, she puffed unerringly. The wonder of the smoke rings and sheer satisfaction delighted me.

I searched F.W.'s good eye for any hint of enlightenment. If it was a lantern unto his soul then it was coated with lampblack. Or, the lights were off and nobody was home.

On the same pack: *In hoc signo vinces*, "In this sign you will conquer." I looked up the meaning during Miss Doan's Latin class. On my way to lunch, I spied her sitting in the teachers' lounge, smoke purling from a cancer stick. She fell asleep in bed and burned up. I figured she'd taken "to the stars" literally. Then, too, her morning breath smelled of bourbon.

I stole a carton of my mother's cigarettes once, but openly confessed. What's the use of lying? She always knew when I wasn't telling the truth, like the time I stayed home to watch John Glenn launch. She applauded my honesty but whipped the backs of my hands with a thin belt. 'If the eye offends you pluck it out, if the hand causes you to sin, cut it off,' she said sternly, hands trembling from withdrawal as she lit a cigarette and took a deep pull. The thing was, I wanted to save her the pain. I was willing to endure hardships so she wouldn't go to the stars. But nicotine, it turns out, was as addictive as heroin, and she never broke its grip.

F.W. blew a steady stream in my face. "Pall Mall," he said, posing like Edward R. Murrow. "Taken from a 17th Century English game with a ball, *palla* and hammer, *malleus*."

"Croquet?" I glanced nervously at the Challenger. How long could they keep the crew sitting on top of those tanks of liquid nitrogen and oxygen?

"Something like that," he said, "Where can I get lunch around here?"

"The Dixie," I said, "Good as any. Just up the street."

He inhaled again and tapped the ash conspicuously on the floor. He rubbed his right eye. Maybe he'd remove it like college days at the University? He'd pluck it out and drop it in his martini like an olive—drink it down and 'voila!' a third eye appeared between his front teeth. Co-eds were repulsed by the stunt, frat brothers regaled it. It wasn't until he married a belly dancer that his talents were truly appreciated.

"They're made in Petersburg," I said.

"Not for long." He leaned forward and coughed hard through stained teeth.

"Outstanding . . . and they are mild!" I said, with the same baritone voice that dunned them on TV.

"Four thousand jobs. All that money, poof, up in smoke!" He laughed.

"You see the irony?"

"Just like Richmond," he said. "So long Tobacco Row."

"There's still plenty of pension money," I said.

"Beautiful office," he said, looking out the window.

"Lowest overhead in the system."

SHUTTLE DELAY scrolled across the TV. Smoke vented from the tanks. F.W. leaned forward and squinted at the small screen.

"Always wanted to do that," he said. "I'm a pilot, you know."

"Never too late for a new career."

"It's a tricky business," F.W. said, "Like any business."

"It doesn't look good." I drummed my fingers.

"All that planning, preparation and money." One eye stared out the window. "Timing and execution. Unintended consequences, like Vietnam. The waste of blood and treasure, idiots running the show."

"*The Peter Principal,*" I said, "raising to your level of

incompetency."

"Sometimes you just have to wave the white flag and say, 'Well we tried,' and walk away," he said.

"They know the risk when they volunteer," I said. "Six days they've been strapped on their backs."

"B & W pours millions of dollars into this community. Now they're leaving and there's nothing to replace it."

"I'd just go for it." I watched the TV absently.

"We needed capital," he said, rubbing his hands together. "Like you said, everybody knows the risk."

"What are we talking about?"

"You," he said, "taking the risk."

"What risk?"

"We're closing this office," F.W. said. He dropped the cigarette into his cup. It doused with a sputter.

"The most profitable office in the company?"

"It's a greedy business," he said. "But I've weathered coups before." Windows rattled.

"That decision isn't up to you anymore," I said.

"Nothing more cut throat than brokers and bankers," he said. "Talk about nets, informants and double agents. Talking is their business and they can't stop. Never met a broker who could keep a secret."

"Always an exception to every generalization."

"By . . . the . . . way, some of your partners decided not to invest. Your little gambit fell short. I'm still majority stockholder." F.W. stood and walked towards the door. "I'm hungry," he said. He turned. "Your brokers will be transferred to Richmond."

"What makes you think that?"

"They volunteered."

"And me?"

"Just like the parable," he said, "Matthew, isn't it? 'Many are called and few are chosen.'" He smiled. "Never too late for a new career."

"And my clients?"

"They'll be in good hands." He stepped through the door.

I followed him downstairs, angry, speechless, not knowing whether to curse his arrogance or admire his guile. As F.W. reached the front door a burst of wind slammed it open. *The Fox Hunt* fluttered and tore loose. He left the door wide-open, wind howling as he walked past his car towards the Dixie. A blinking barricade somersaulted like a gymnast but landed flat on its back. I slammed the door.

The bullpen was empty. Elsa typed furiously, bit her lip and wouldn't look up.

"Where's everyone?"

"Early lunch."

"You knew, didn't you?" I said.

"You hear things," she said. "Here's your paperwork. Want something to drink?"

"Hemlock." I said. "The brokers won't be back. Cancel my appointments and take the rest of the day off." She nodded and reached for her coat.

I closed the door and sat. The TV switched coverage to *The Price Is Right*. Bob Barker talked to a contestant in front of a large wheel. The burly woman with fat ankles bid on a boat and all expense paid vacation to Rome. A picture of the coliseum flashed.

I looked out the window and down at F.W.'s car, the crumbled blocks, barricade lights blinking. I dialed Captain Lowery, Police Department.

"Morning captain," I said. "Hell of a blow last night." We bantered.

"Someone left their car out front last night. Looks like it's been damaged. Could you send a wrecker and have it towed? Thanks." Living in a small town had its perks. Breakfast with the police chief at Kiwanis was one of them.

Half-hour later brakes screeched, hydraulics hissed as a bar lifted the Citroen.

"That's my car!" F.W. yelled, his voice snatched away.

"Well it's a tow zone," said the driver. "Besides, you can't drive it with a block through the window."

"What the hell?"

"Can't you read? NO PARKING/TOW ZONE?"

"This is my office," he said. "Mine! My brokers, my rugs, my furniture, mine!" F.W. cried out with West End incredulity. He kicked at the heavy oak doors. "I don't know how," he yelled, "But I know you had something to do with this."

"You can ride to city impound and pay the charge," the driver said. "Then I'll haul it wherever you want." I opened the window as the truck pulled away. F.W. looked up.

"Plausible," I yelled. He rolled down the window but the driver wouldn't stop.

"What?" His hand cupped his ear.

"Plausible," I yelled. "That's the key." Small consolation, I smiled and gave a middle finger salute. The tow truck turned the corner and was gone.

The TV picture cut away to the launch pad at Cape Canaveral. I turned up the sound, " . . . three, two, one, zero." Engines ignited, a torrent of smoke and flame washed over the pad, boosters firing, hold down bolts exploded. "We have *lift off*!"

The Challenger's silver wings lifted majestically like a home sick angel. I cranked the sound all the way up to hear that special crackling STS-1 engine; 418,000 pounds of thrust. It sent a bolt up my spine, same as when I was a kid.

"You are a go at throttle up," a TV voice said.

"Roger, go at throttle up," shuttle commander, Dick Scobee said.

Ten seconds later, a voice from shuttle said, "Uh oh," and something exploded in a massive ball of smoke and flame. Two boosters broke free from the oxygen tank and corkscrewed across the sky.

"Flight controllers here are looking very carefully at the situation," Steve Nesbitt, public affairs officer, said.

The solid boosters collapsed, tore loose from the shuttle and painted a double helix across the blue sky. The shuttle wings sheered off as the crew cabin reached 65,000 feet, lost momentum and fell fluttering like Icarus into the sea. All that was left were Os hanging listlessly in the cold blue sky.

"*Sweet Jesus!*" I struck the keyboard with my fist then punched it with my index finger over and over, filling the screen with zeros.

I closed my eyes, slumped back in my chair. One minute you're sitting on top expecting a smooth ride and next minute you're at the bottom of the sea. I should have learned that as a kid. We passed the billboard where the smoking hot blond had always been, she was gone—the sign torn down and hauled away.

"Where is she?" I asked.

My father glanced in the mirror and shrugged, puffed on his stogie. I searched my mother's face for an explanation as she fished for the last cigarette in her pack and lit up. She tilted her head back and blew an O, for the first time. But her head wasn't poised at that perfect angle. Her lips were neither round nor red, hair wasn't quaffed but her eyes were wide with desperation. As she exhaled that O I recognized that the gaiety of my billboard blond had been replaced by nothing more than a tawdry habit. The physical contentment on my mothers face bore sad resemblance to despair. The mysterious Os were nothing more than empty lies, fueled by addiction. But then again we all have addictions, at once masking and exposing our tolerance for pain.

I opened the window, hoisted the TV on my shoulder and stepped wobbly onto the ledge. Atlas shrugged as tin foil broke loose from antennas and fluttered down like filigree. Glass shattered, fractals rippled; knobs and nozzles skipped like rocks across a pond. Plastic ribs, circuitry and sad remnants splintered.

I locked up, walked to the Dixie and took a seat in my booth. Rotisserie dogs spun in perpetual motion, primordial ooze bubbled in the crockpot.

"Two dogs, all the way," I said.

My eyes were drawn toward the high-pitched whistle of the Lionel train as it circled the room and passed overhead. Small Os puffed from the engine's smoke stack. It gave a subtle reminder with familiar reprise. The truth was simple—everyone lies. The LBO was a roll of the dice. It turns out, rolling snake eyes gave meaning, satisfaction and connectedness with the past and a destiny of my choosing.

I removed the training schedule from my brief case. MUTA-6 three-day flyaway; Key West scuba, scout swim, night infil techniques and shots at Papa Joe's until the crack of dawn. *Per aspera ad astra.*

BLACK HAND

Sitting in the open door of a UH-1D Huey, 1200 AGL, a frigid wind burned my face. A kaleidoscope of colors streamed through broken clouds. The cold brown earth blended with budding trees and spring wheat on this, the cruelest day of the year.

The wind tossed chopper pitched and yawed like a ship, foundering at sea. Its tail boom drifted sideways as the nose dipped and rose. My stiff fingers flexed inside black gloves and rested on my reserve chute. Legs dangled out the door. A yellow static line snaked from my MC1-1 parachute to a D-ring in the middle of the cabin floor. Time for my monthly adrenaline fix, courtesy of U.S. Army, Special Forces Reserve. A rucksack balanced on my shins as I checked the rubber bands that secured the drop line; fingered the quick release straps. It was a lousy day to jump equipment but orders is orders.

The earth curved as a red-tailed hawk circled below; rode

eddies and updrafts. Airborne mythology—hawks fly, bad shit happens. Seemed like the hawk flew every time we jumped this drop zone. Last time out four troopers hit the runway, two medevaced with broken bones. Luck or skill, I hit pay dirt. Any jump you walk away from is a good jump.

At 1200 feet above Fort Pickett airfield, the crisscross of runways resembled a kite frame. I closed one eye and aimed my jump boot at the inverted L that marked the drop zone, DZ. Major Wilson, company commander, Pancho Villa mustache, sat in the number-one slot beside me. Tradition dictated that he play wind dummy on first pass; determine if the wind was calm enough for the rest of us to jump. Wilson sneered and glanced my way. He worked hard to cultivate a certain élan, calm men's fears or at the least, disguise his own. If Wilson burned in they'd scratch the company jump. The jumpmaster tapped his helmet and said, "Goooo!"

Major machismo gave a thumbs-up, pressed hands to the floor, hoisted ass and pushed off. I watched and counted, as the fifteen-foot static line stretched like a bungee cord, extended risers and pulled a slim green cocoon from his deployment bag. The chute blossomed as he passed beneath the chopper out of sight. I stuffed my black gloves under my chest harness, edged forward and checked my boot knife for easy retrieval. Tree landings were always in play on windy days.

Green smoke streamed low and fast across the DZ as we circled. A stiff windsock extended from the tower. Winds were marginal, 10 to 15, gusting to 20. Blasts of cold air made the calculation tricky for the DZSO, drop zone safety officer.

The equation: forward throw, drift and dispersion, depended on wind speed. Gusting winds made the whole exercise a crapshoot. I blew on my fingers—seven come eleven.

I felt a deep, hard, thump, thump, thump vibrate through the cold metal floor. The drumbeat pulsed through my body. Something hot formed near the tip of my ass bone. The visceral thwack of rotors, pitch and yaw, metallic judder, activated a kind of molten slag that shot up my spine. Ore from a smelting ladle poured into my brainpan and my sight whited out.

I stared, frozen with fear and curiosity as I floated outside the chopper; peered into its cabin, disembodied and digitized, monochromatic, beneath a quiet blur of blades. I watched a jumper sitting with his long legs out the door, rucksack balanced on shins, as he stuffed black gloves into his parachute harness, edged forward and touched his boot knife. The jumpmaster struck his helmet and said "Gooo!" Swept away, he fell endlessly, back in time.

I blinked hard and forced my eyes wide. The countryside reappeared with stark revision. The beige ground of Southside Virginia transformed to jungle green, sky, cobalt blue, clouds had a cotton ball hue. The Annamese Mountains appeared below, a vast expanse of triple canopy jungle, lush and forbidding. It spread as far as the eye and flat Sargasso Sea.

A vivid film played behind my eyes as I dropped back in time and space, one body and mind, in the here and now sitting in the open door of a UH-1D flying over Co Roc Mountain. The Laotian landmark, an immense sheer of rock, rose just beyond the Vietnam border. Crowned with lush vegetation, concentric trails ringed its imposing edifice. The pilot pointed towards the checkpoint—as distinct and treacherous as the Matterhorn. We turned south and dropped rapidly into the Ashau Valley on final approach.

I scanned the triple canopy for movement; trails, metallic glints, elephants, tigers, or even a rare muntjac deer, short pointy horns, but mostly for flashes and green tracers drifting up silently, bird beaks pecking on the aluminum hull. I searched for the pitifully small island in the green sea, a sad and impossible landing zone. I leaned forward, black gloves, Car-15 rifle, rucksack, ammo, water, rations, PRC-77 radio and the fucking KY-38 encryption device with extra batteries, twenty pounds of dead weight that rarely worked.

Beside me sat Chen, Lau, and Troung; slack-faced and eager. Sergeant Elders, Chau, Con and Mau sat in the other door; tightly wound and ready to spring. I was at once in the now and then, synapse firing in the frontal cortex. A rush and hum of electrical currents pulsed through my body. My motor revved, fueled by the prospects of an odious fate, threatened to tear from its mounts. The baby-faced crew chief, wool flight suit, M-60, strafed the wood line on final approach, grinned and gave thumbs up.

"Goooo!"

A distant slap on my back and I looked down. We were above the tree line, way too high to jump. The fall wouldn't kill me but the weight of my ruck would shred my knees or break my back. The Nungs couldn't carry me. My heels locked against the skids and I didn't jump.

"Goooo!" Again, a hand hit my back. I looked at Chen with that what-the-fuck look and gave over to muscle memory, unsure of where I'd hit, Laos or Narnia.

"Gooooo!"

My airborne training triggered a knee jerk response. I tensed as I dropped toward the landing zone, LZ, free-falling, listening for the audible snap of a leg, knees ripping, back cracking as my hundred pound ruck drove me like a pylon into the ground.

But I just floated. I felt a jerk from behind and chafe of wind on my face. I looked around for Lau, Chen and Troung suspended in that void, at once falling dimly, then oddly, kneeling on the ground trying to send an encrypted message from my one time pad, plain text paired with random key. I whispered hurriedly each phonetic letter into the KY-38 handset, our lifeline, with the gray winged Cessna circling in updrafts and eddies. The ripple of small arms fire snapped through the leaves and Lau pointed to a dark hole in the jungle, three fingers, enemy flanking. I whispered urgently but my petition went unanswered. The KY-38 was on the fritz again and Covey couldn't hear, let alone decode my message. I may as well have been talking into a string can. A company of *bo dai*s wedged in belt buckle tight against my team, braced for the pounding from TAC air.

"*Motherfucker*!" I ripped off the cable, grabbed the handset and transmitted in the open, "*Prairie Fire!*" The heavy contact and my declaration meant that Covey had to pull us out, now!

Covey's voice filtered through the triple canopy jungle into my ear. "Break contact and continue the mission." What the fuck? Unbeknownst to me, someone had added a codicil to what turned out to be my revocable trust. Trust meant when I said, "We're in contact" the deadly game of hide and seek was over, and they'd come for me, unquestionably.

We weren't kids playing 'guns' in the woods behind our house. There were no timeouts here, no arguments about sucking chest wounds. And who amongst us could rise from the dead, choose up sides and play war again?

A B-40 rocket exploded, sideswiped the tree above me. I gave the hand and arm signal to break contact, *didi mau*. Chen cranked off a claymore, initiated IA, immediate action drill. We'd practiced it a thousand times. I punched a toe popper in the ground, pulled the safety and covered it hurriedly.

Each man fired a clip on full automatic, then retreated to the end of the file, took a knee and reloaded. The trick, during controlled chaos, was not to fire before the man in front cleared. When shit started flying the trigger finger got twitchy. It was easy to get stitched from behind by your own man. The tail gunner waited a few seconds after the last man cleared. The charging enemy hit a wall of ball bearings as the claymore exploded. Going was slow in the thick jungle. Minutes later an explosion and muffled scream came from behind. A *bo dai's* foot transformed into bloody hamburger. The wounded comrade would slow the lead tracker.

I snapped awake from this vision, looked up and

followed my suspension lines to the skirt of the parachute. A camouflaged dome fixed and filled above my head. I struggled to recalculate my whereabouts and managed to gauge my altitude, two hundred feet over the DZ. While my drop and turn rate were okay, my forward speed was double what it should be. I was headed for a small dirt patch between an intersection of three concrete runways. I turned into the wind and took up a good body position for landing; legs bent, toes pointed and elbows tucked. A burst of wind took my chute. I pulled down on the toggles and popped them, pulled quick release straps; dropped ruck, gripped the risers and pulled down.

I bounced along the runway; a manikin flung from a speeding pickup. Flipping face down towards the runway, I puckered for a kiss. I maintained the tight landing position; elbows pressed tightly into my rib cage. The smooth grey surface rushed up towards my patrician nose. I blinked just before hitting the cement and my brain short-circuited airborne training. My arm extended reflexively and stiff-armed the ground. Physics reasserted its domain and something snapped. My arm slammed into a concretized world. In a rock, scissors, paper world, cement was salutatorian.

My steel pot gonged, head rattled, as I smacked the runway. Blue-green bubbles filled my head. Though my nose and pearly whites had been spared, there came the distinct sound of one hand smashing. The concrete sand papered my ass and chewed leather jump boots as I dragged along. If I could release the suspension lines, the chute would deflate and end the wild ride. I reached across my chest and squeezed the quick release button on the shoulder harness. Nothing happened.

I glanced down where my right hand should be, but something bent and bloated extended at a curious angle. A hideous lump of pretzel dough flopped along side, useless as Chen's severed hand. A burst of wind inflated my canopy and I was off to the races. Planing out at motor-cross speeds, I squeezed the safety release button on the other shoulder. I squeezed hard but it was jammed.

A new recruit, posted along the runway, sprang to life and sprinted towards the apex of my chute. If he couldn't catch it the wind would blow me into the next county.

"Lay *on* MacDuff!" I yelled. Alice, my rucksack, drug behind; pouches ripped and flapping like dog-ears. MacDuff's first training day provided him with critical airborne experience, a puppy chasing sheets. He grabbed the apex and swung my chute into the wind. The canopy fluttered and died.

My torso rested on the hardpan, legs on the runway. A dust devil danced across my helmet as I took inventory. My boots were gouged. Something near the end of my arm twisted backwards; spoiled hamburger, bloated and black. It had, no doubt, fallen out of my busted rucksack. Specialist MacDuff bent over to catch his breath.

"You O-K, sir?" MacDuff asked.

"*Airborne!*" Mantra. Universal; means nothing and everything, like hoorah! Lying there I tried to figure how I'd zipped through time, recursive, outside looking in or vice versa, or was this even my body? An old trick enabled me to at once embrace and ignore pain. In this line of work discipline was essential and denial, de rigueur.

MacDuff straightened, scanned my arm and knitted his brow.

"Jesus, sir." His face, a rictus of revulsion, turned green. "I'll get help." He took three steps, doubled over and puked. He straightened and started for the ambulance at the far end of the DZ.

"Get me *up!*" I ordered.

MacDuff dissolved into a purple haze, lips moving without sound. A gust of wind snatched his boonie hat and spun it like a frisbee across the field.

"This ain't my first rodeo!"

"But, sir . . ." he stammered.

"Damn it, where's Sergeant Elder?" If MacDuff couldn't get the job done, Elder would. He'd police up that busted hand and find its owner.

Someone yelled from across the airfield, "The *hawk* is out!"

A shadow passed overhead. Sergeant McMillan, team medic, eyes locked on the tree line, tucked tight for a five-point landing but smacked the ground with a single vicious thud, crumpled like a morning dove. He dragged limply behind his chute. Another recruit, head cocked; Nipper staring at a gramophone, watched as jumpers corkscrewed in.

"Get after him!" I shouted. Nipper raced the wrong way. "*Medic! Medic!*" Instead of the jumpers, he ran towards the ambulance.

I unsnapped my reserve, hit the quick release button at the center of my webbing and slipped out of the harness. I was determined to walk away, but first I had to stand. The ground spun, head rung as I tried haltingly to kneel. Maybe I should wait for Elders. I swatted blue gnats and ignored the church bells.

SFC Courtney, company medic, quick timed toward me. His shoulders swayed—exaggerated like a boxer taking center ring. He had a pug nose and puffed scar over the right eye, titivating like a tattoo.

"So much for that big right hand," Pug said. He squatted and removed my helmet, elevated my feet. We'd boxed Golden Gloves, traded punches, swapped sweat; beat each other without objection.

"Hammer hand?" I asked. Gainfully employed as a detective between drills, I was confident Pug would find the owner of that hand. His fingers outlined my dented helmet. He gathered crime scene evidence and revealed a working theory.

"More like hammer head, sir," he said.

"You my cut man?"

"I'm the tow truck, sir," said Pug. "You've been in a wreck." He put two fingers on my carotid and checked pupils.

"Darvon and drive on!" I said.

"Not today." He snapped his fingers. "You took a big hit and you're going into shock." He opened his M-5 medical bag and unrolled some chicken wire. "I'm going to splint your hand."

I looked down. "That's not mine."

"Well I'm going to splint it until we find the owner," he said.

"Must be Chen's." I flashed back, Laos, firefight, bo dai closing. As I looked around for the Nung striker, his body lifted effortlessly, hand cleaved like a pork chop.

"Stick with me here," Pug said. He clapped his hands. "You're a little wonky."

"How many fingers?" I asked, holding up my middle. "Just find Sergeant Elder." He looked like G.I. Joe. I looked around for his dark profile, square jaw and three-day beard. Nothing cartoonish about him, he was serious business.

"Newly assigned to the company?" Pug asked. He wrapped the pusillanimous pile with chicken wire and left it resting on my stomach.

"It must be Chen's," I said. Elder had tied off the stump and got the IV going as the team laid down a heavy base of fire. I reloaded a clip, spotted his hand and picked it up. It felt warm as a three-pound glove. The fingers curled into a fist and I dropped it. I cursed and stowed it in my ruck. Maybe they could sew it back on. The blast from a rocket flattened me as I pressed the handset to my ear.

"Fast movers, inbound," Covey said.

"Heads down!" I yelled. Roiling clouds of napalm swept across our front, devouring every living thing. I ducked my head as a fiery explosion sucked the air from my lungs.

Pug gave thumbs up as MacDuff and Nipper carried me to the medevac chopper and slid the stretcher into the door. The crew chief said, "We're taking you to Portsmouth Naval

Hospital, should take about three-zero." The high-pitched whine of engines, sweet smell of avgas and the thump of the rotors sent me back in time, surrounded in the Ashau, as I called for a Prairie Fire extraction.

SOG missions were supposed to be 'sneak and peak' along the Ho Chi Minh Road, gather intelligence and get out. Once we found the enemy, or they found us, we were done. But somehow the new number crunching, fast-tracked West Point leg commander, had altered our contract, added a codicil.

> *"The aforementioned agreement under paragraph 4 page 31 of a SOG, Emergency Extraction, hereafter known as "Prairie Fire" shall be subject to the sole discretion of commander, who may otherwise countermand said team leader, hereafter, "One Zero," and order him to "Break contact and continue the mission" regardless of intervening actions or consequences. The One Zero shall hold harmless the "commander" for any death, dismemberment or wounding suffered by any team member, to include but not limited to capture."*

Instead of the team leader running the show, a self-appointed intercessor could refuse my collect call. The recording said, "Break contact and continue mission." I phoned Covey again as a company of NVA laid down a blistering volley of fire and prepared to rush. A sortie of Spad's circled to the south, buzzards sniffing carrion. The team collapsed into tight perimeter as Covey marked the enemy with smoke.

"Danger close," Covey said.

"Perilous!" I yelled into the handset.

The roar of 20mm cannons deafened us; shredding all vegetation and life forms into mulch. Next came 250 pounders, explosions erupting like Vesuvius as the A-1Es worked the ridgeline and finally the coup de grace; napalm erupting into a fiery Armageddon. We moved out smartly. The smell of burnt hair and charred bone was choking. I coughed and opened my eyes.

The smooth glow of haloes, lux luminaries, circled and elevated me as I floated in a white beam of sterile light. The white sheet draped over me meant I'd either volunteered for a magic trick or the mother ship had just finished the anal probe. The sweet acidulous smell of astringent stung the nose but complimented flowery notes of iodine and alcohol. Muffled mutterings, footsteps and the rattle of gurney wheels blended with swooshing sounds of swinging doors.

"Where's the X-ray?" the voice said.

Something slick and tuberous probed my ear. I tightened my sphincter and wondered if aliens knew the benefits of K-Y Jelly. A hand forced my mouth open. Fingers pried at my eyelids. Penlight flashed across my iris. "The vitreous humor looks like marmalade," he said. "I'm Major Powell." Dark round eyes magnified by his thick glasses; the owl blinked.

"You're at Portsmouth Naval Hospital, captain."

This was worse than I thought. I'd died and come back as a squid. The steady drip of the IV and bleep, bleep of a machine did not reassure. Maybe they're making me bionic. Always wanted a jackhammer dick.

"You've got a concussion and a shattered wrist," Owl said. "Your vitals are stable. We need to review your anamnesis."

"I don't remember?" I squinted at his skinny beak.

"That's amnesia," he said. His head swiveled as he slipped a stethoscope into his white smock. Talons clawed at my bruised ribs and organs. "Anamnesis is your medical history."

"No, I mean, I can't remember," I said, "Did Chen make it out?"

The exam table cranked slowly into sitting position as a nurse, white-faced kabuki, removed the IV and unplugged the electronics. The green blip went flat on the florescent screen and died. A plastic skeleton hung á la cart with slack jawed grin in the corner. A blue plastic band circled my wrist. Owl's hair parted like feathers in the middle of his forehead. As he flipped through the chart he mumbled and lifted the hand off the sheet. He inspected the bruised fruit. Something suspicious was going on here. Maybe they'd tried to sew that hideous thing on my arm while I was out. Good thing they'd failed. It was one pulverized puppy.

"Where'd that come from?" I asked. They didn't seem to know what the hell was going on with the hand or with my flitting back and forth in time—and I couldn't tell them. They'd think I was making it up. I'd be crazy not to be a little paranoid.

Owl prodded the swollen skin, black as a banana, inspected it; lingered over metacarpal lumps on the ring and middle finger. "These bones are depressed."

"Wouldn't you be?"

The doc clamped an X-ray on the light box and flipped on the switch. The neon sign blinked on. "How'd you break those?"

"Memory dulls." He had twenty questions and I had zero answers.

"Boxer?" he chided.

"Remind me." I tried to reel in memory but there was nothing on the other end of the line. The deeper I cast the less I retrieved. I gave up and cut bait.

"X-rays don't lie," he said.

"You'd see right through me."

"Hmmm." He studied a full-blown chest X-ray; pointed to a white line that extended down the arm from the shoulder. He lifted the sleeve of my T-shirt. His fingers traced a thick, fibrous scar, snaking from shoulder cap to elbow joint. He eyed a diamond back tattoo; its rattler inked at one end and head poised to strike at the other.

"Nice tats," Owl said.

"Tequila," I said. "The worm offered bitter advice."

"Tear of the mid-substance biceps branchii muscle belly," Owl said. He shifted his gaze to the white phalanx of fingers spread across the black X-ray.

"You've got a flexion fracture of the radius," he said. "We've got work to do."

He rolled the skeleton from the corner, lifted its limp arm and pointed to the wrist. "All of this bone is gone." He pointed to white specks that blotted out the otherwise black X-ray. He squeezed the pasty dough where the wrist used to be, "This is powdered bone."

"What about that?" I pointed to something jagged like a bayonet.

"Reductio," he said, pedantically. Owl pushed the skeleton aside and rolled a steel rod with a T-bar welded at the top next to me.

"Ad absurdum?" The diagnosis was weak. Couldn't he follow logic? There lays a black and detached hand on a sheet. It's not mine. Case closed.

"This device will enlist gravity and reduce that small sack of flour back into a loosely configured wrist." Owl pointed to five metallic clips, Chinese handcuffs hanging from a T-bar. He poked the wrist with his index finger. It dimpled like bread dough.

"I love the smell of biscuits in the morning."

"We'll stick your fingers in those clamps."

"How many times I got to tell you? That's not mine!"

One by one, Owl pulled the curled fingers from a fist, looking more and more like Chen's severed hand. He clamped them into Chinese handcuffs until he came to a frozen pinky, curled like a C. He couldn't get it to fit.

"Interesting," Owl said. He traced scars on the back of the hand. "Looks like they removed muscle for a flexor tendon repair?

"That is one evil hand," I said.

"How'd that happen?"

"How the hell should I know? Maybe the damn thing was holding a glass when it decided to punch somebody in the face."

"That's one bad ass hand."

"A mind of its own," I said, "Find the owner. He should be held responsible." The brazen Owl maintained his charade, kept the gnarly hand, wrist and forearm hanging nearby. I wanted nothing to do with it. Owl lifted a ten-pound weight.

"I'm going to lay this on your bicep to accelerate reduction." He pointed to the skeleton's arm, three inches below the elbow and above the wrist. "We'll drill holes through the radius and ulna, insert pins here and here. Then we'll drill through the metacarpals and insert a pin through the back of the hand." Owl covered the hand with a red handkerchief.

"Lie back and relax. When I remove the handkerchief, the owner will magically appear." Owl said.

"Mox nix to me," I said. "How long before I'm back in the field?" Shots of morphine were temporary but would suffice for now. All too soon they would fade and I'd need that airborne rush. My body, held together by pins and wire, was driven by some unexamined and existential conviction that I could train men how to survive the next war. And there *would* be a next war. Question was, would the price I'd paid for all this wreckage enable my men survive the next one, or keep me from surviving the last one?

"As far as your anamnesis," Owl said, "Your body keeps the score."

The bright, round interrogation lamp bore down and I confessed, "I don't care."

"What is it with you guys?" Owl said. "Hell bent for . . ."

"Just find Chen. They've got to be working on him around here somewhere." I laid-back, awash in light, confused but convinced that time slid back and forth as easy as the zipper on my fly.

I looked at the hand and felt a sucking sensation, snatched backwards through a rushing wind. I struggled to focus, looked down fifty feet off the jungle floor in my Swiss Seat, D ring thread thru a handhold. Spinning, I gripped the nylon rope as the helicopter drug me through the thick tangle of vines ripping at me, limbs slapping my face. I caught my last fleeting glimpse of Chen propped against a tree, empty albumin bag, IV tube, holding his bloody stump, glassy-eyed and forever dead.

I opened my eyes and stared into two saucers, Owl snapping his fingers.

"Haven't seen Chen but I've got a Sergeant MacMillan in the next room," Owl said, "We're shipping him to Walter Reed, first available chopper."

"Hand?"

"Broken back," Owl said, "How does that song go, . . . '*he ain't gonna jump no more?*'"

A palmist logo, fingers spread, cast its shadow on the handkerchief. If what Owl said was true—that hand was somebody's scoreboard. I lifted the handkerchief and stared at the wreckage. Owl stood by.

"Talk to the hand," Owl said. He extended his palm toward my face.

"I don't understand." He was speaking code.

"Universal language," Owl said, "We're hard-wired for pain."

"And the scoreboard?" I asked.

"People only get the message when they've had enough pain," Owl said. "Men of your caliber have a inordinate capacity for self-denial. Some are just numb. You're a combination of both."

I closed my eyes, took a deep breath. The heaviness on my chest sank to the pit of my stomach. In time my head cleared. Maybe I'd lugged the pain of Vietnam around all these years, heavy and useless as that KY-38. I'd ignored the messages, cryptic or chronic; dreams and night sweats from the underground. It was as if I'd ignored an insurgency, deep within. Everything about me, even my code of conduct, was broke. But if I remembered the pain, used it sparingly, maybe that gnarly, black hand could pen a story that even I could understand.

YELLOW HORSE

Million Chinks comin' through the pass
Playin' burp-gun boogie all over my ass
I'm movin' on, I'll soon be gone
With my M-1 broke, it ain't no joke
I'll soon be gone.

The Bug-Out Ballad
8th Cavalry, Korea, 1950

Not that you don't hear some overripe bullshit about it: tumbling dominoes, maintaining the equilibrium of the Dingdong by containing the ever-encroaching Doohah; you could hear some young soldier in all bloody innocence saying, 'All that's just a load, man. We're here to kill gooks. Period.

Michael Herr, *Dispatches*

In 1961, Pete Starr and Terry Moore enlisted in the army during their junior year of high school. Three years younger at the time and sick of school, I imagined the adventure was like running away to Buffalo Bill's Wild West circus. Pete and Terry joined on the buddy system, finished Advanced Training and were shipped to Korea; further assigned to 2nd Battalion, 7th Cavalry, 2/7, The Ghost Battalion. Almost wiped out during the Battle of Pusan Perimeter in 1950, it withstood relentless attacks by the North Korean Army; counterattacked and broke out.

The 1/7th Cavalry was General George Armstrong Custer's unit. They officially adopted an Irish drinking tune and nickname, Gary Owen. The First Cavalry was annihilated at the Battle of Little Big Horn, August 8th 1876. The Lokata called it the Battle of Greasy Grass, made slick by blood from all the dead horses. It wasn't much of a battle. The arrogant Boy General split his forces and led his men to slaughter. A hundred years later the 1/7th was nearly overrun in Vietnam on LZ X-Ray, Ia (Ya) Drang Valley, November, 1965. Surrounded and vastly outnumbered by NVA they stood and fought; survived by sheer grit, the grace of God, and most important, TAC Air. Imagine what Custer could have done with napalm.

On a cold, dreary, November day, seven days before Veteran's Day, and eleven before the anniversary of LZ-X-Ray, I sat alone, reading *The Living And The Dead,* by Paul Hendrickson. The book was about lies old men tell youth when they send them off to war. After the French lost the Battle of Dien Bien Phu, 1954, and were kicked out of Vietnam, President Eisenhower explained why the U.S. should take up the mantle. "You have this row of dominoes set up, knock over the first one and what will happen to the last one is the certainty it will go over very quickly." Called the domino theory, Presidents Kennedy and Johnson parroted the line.

As I flipped the pages faster, harkened back to Nam's disaster, the air grew denser, perfumed from an unseen censer, came a rapping on my door. I expected the shadow in the window to skirt through the breezeway like before.

I cracked open the three-inch thick oak door of what people on Reed Street called The Bunker. The walls, poured in 1946, were concrete and rebar. Summer nights they radiated like a brick oven—winter, cold as a coffin.

The two-bedroom blockhouse had a small, reinforced fallout shelter, where I stashed the washer-dryer and LuRP rations. Its Spanish façade was block and plaster. The flat tar roof, parapet with rolling arches and fighting wall resembled the Alamo and conformed to siege mentality. The block wall along the front porch channeled avenues of approach but restricted fields of fire. From the living room I surveilled a T-intersection through four slim gun port windows.

I cracked the front door. "How'd you find me?" I asked. So much for living on the down low. Life was hard enough without interlopers.

Hawk-nosed Pete, black cap, hadn't changed since high school; curly brown hair and Coke bottle glasses but without taped frames from fistfights. He left school just before the Beatles' first big hit, *Love Me Do*, about the time cockney accents and Beatle cuts entered the lexicon of screaming teenyboppers. His timing was notoriously poor.

"You ever think about getting a phone?" Pete said. He eyed the canvas throw cloth, paintbrushes and cans.

"Who needs a phone?" I said. "People . . . things, appear just in time."

This house, for example, found me in a sad state of disrepair. Bought by a friend in foreclosure, I volunteered to plug the hole in the roof, scrub moldy walls, scrape tile, rip out the kitchen, plaster the walls and rebuild the parapet, in lieu of a modest rent. Better than living in a car.

Pete's family emigrated from England in the 50's. He had a queer, cockney accent that drove Virginia rednecks to distraction. His Napoleonic complex, dry sense of humor and uncanny capacity for trouble didn't help. In spite of his peculiarities he was a gifted artist, mercurial, Van Gogh. He still had both ears, though cauliflowered.

"How many years?" I asked. I scanned the breezeway, half-expecting the scraggy specter of the Vietnam veteran who'd once lived here. If a house symbolized the soul, then he'd *slud* into the quagmire. The bunker had partnered in similar decay.

"My wedding?" Pete squinted. "I forget, but that was one hell-ov-a bachelor party." He offered an opened case of beer.

"Glad they didn't catch you." I pictured Pete streaking, fleet-footed Hermes in patent leather shoes, across the 18th green at the club chased by two rent-a-cops.

"Want one?" Pete glanced down at the loose beers, smiled sheepishly and tucked in his shirttail.

"Gave it up," I said. "Two years, sixteen days."

"Sorry to hear that," Pete said. He juggled the loose cans. Half the beers were gone.

"You lost?"

"*We Light the Way*," he said, stepping proudly inside. "Pathfinder motto."

"You must've been on the trail a while," I said. His sour breath and clothes reeked.

"Lost my bearings."

"How'd the marriage work out?" I asked. Fresh air stirred the fumes.

"Could be summed up as, three strikes and you're out." He surveyed the blank oatmeal walls of the bunker, no curtains and mismatch of yard sale furniture. Stepping around a ladder and paint tray, he pulled off his jacket and collapsed into a mauve La-Z-Boy in front of the fireplace. I sat as he popped a beer and took a hard pull.

"Ever go to the War Memorial?"

"Once," I said. "Not my cup of tea."

"I see the Colonel on Veteran's Day," Pete said. "I'm Color Guard Commander for the VFW. We post colors, do funerals and such."

"Fuck the VFW," I said. "Didn't treat us kindly after Vietnam. Said we lost the war. Not the five Presidents, Congress, the Joint Chiefs. The fucking grunts lost the war? The greatest de-generation. We bled, same as them."

"Isn't that a little harsh?"

"What'd they know about counter insurgency: terrorism, unconventional warfare, pacification, burn the village to save it, or the Ho Chi Minh Road?"

"We all had our turn in the barrel."

"Patton's Third Army had a Forward Edge of Battle Area, a frontline with good guys on one side and bad guys on the other. The ground you stood on in Vietnam was our FEBA. Mama san, baby san, they'd just as soon frag your ass as look at you. The corruption, spies and VC sympathizers spread from top to bottom. No flag waving freedom fighters along the roads urging you on to Paris."

"I'm Post Commandant," Pete said. He shifted nervously in his seat. "It's not like that now."

"Who needs 'em?" I glanced at the fireplace; black spackled creosote, charred logs crumpled in ash.

"We Light the Way," Pete said.

"Not a flag waving kind of guy."

"You know I served with the 2nd Cav in Korea, redeployed to Fort Benning in '65," he said. "They made us into the 1st Air-Cav."

"*We Were Soldiers Once and Dumb*. I read the book."

"Funny, you went in about the time I got out." Radiator pipes creaked and moaned.

Pete's shoulders were disproportionate to his slim waist. He pumped iron—curls for arms, bench press for chest. Never worked lower body so his Popeye biceps contrasted oddly with Olive Oyl legs.

"The Colonel took me to the barbershop for a G.I. cut, skin tight, then drove me to the recruiter and swore me in," I said. "SFC Ramirez looked at my induction papers, grinned and said, 'Happy Birthday.'"

"Always respected the Colonel," Pete said. "Looked up to him—a no bullshit kind of guy."

"On his last legs."

"Sorry to hear."

"You won't see him soon."

"I got out in September, just before the Cav deployed in

'65." Pete's jaw locked and he swallowed hard. He removed his black cap with Pathfinder pin and Air Assault Badge centered above a 1st Cavalry patch; black horse head silhouette on yellow background divided by a black diagonal line. He slowly traced its outline with his finger.

"The horse we never rode, the line we never crossed and the yellow speaks for itself," chided Pete.

Pete missed senior year history otherwise he would have known that the 7th Cavalry drove all the way to Pyonyang and crossed the Yalu River, which was above the 38th Parallel, which, according to Pete, was the line they never crossed. That slogan was actually dreamed up after the 8th Cavalry was surrounded and annihilated at the Battle of Unan, 1950. Halberstam wrote about it in *The Coldest Winter*. He died shortly after he finished the book. A student chauffeuring him around San Francisco turned the wrong way down a one-way street. All those years on Tu Do Street and he gets whacked in the Golden City.

"Ever tell you about when I got out?"

Pete drubbed his fingers on the top of a beer can, squinted and pushed his glasses off the bridge of his nose. Warm air from steam radiators condensed on cement walls; rivulets puddled on the floor. He shed his sweater and unbuttoned his shirt.

"I was gung-ho when I came back from Korea, graduated Pathfinder and Air Assault School," Pete said. "The battalion trained hard. Just before the unit deployed, First Sergeant Lukevitch handed me some papers and said, 'Your time's up unless you take a burst of four.' I had to reenlist for four more years to get the experience of a lifetime and Uncle Sam would gladly throw in $100 a month for combat pay."

He finished his beer, crumpled the can and dropped it. I stood, walked to the kitchen, poured three-day old coffee and nuked it. Pete popped another beer and rolled up his shirtsleeves, a politician stumping for election.

"It took a few minutes to figure my chances of returning from Vietnam. I figured it was more like the police action in Korea, but halfway around the world in a malaria infested, booby trapped, sniper-ridden jungle. All that appealed to my sense of adventure and camaraderie with the men of first platoon; "A" Company, brothers in arms. I figured all that training was sweat equity. What the hell was it good for if I didn't use it? Wouldn't it all just be a waste of time and energy? I wanted to know!"

"Whether you'd ride the horse and cross the line," I said.

"Doesn't everybody?"

"If the yellow speaks for itself?"

Which anyone that's been in a firefight will tell you is bullshit. It's fight or flight, neurons firing and biochemistry: cortisol and adrenaline, heroin surging through your veins or freezing in place. "Freezing up" to the uninformed, equates to being yellow, cowardly. Most everyone freezes the first time shit hits the fan. It's how we've been hard wired to survive. It's nothing to be ashamed of—I'm not.

"I was ready to make staff sergeant, lead a platoon. It felt righteous." Pete nodded fiercely—studied my face for any hint of judgment.

I waited for his next move; maybe he'd retrieve a lie detector hidden under the front seat of his car, hook it up and prove positively that he'd been ready to charge across that line. Vietnam, split in half in 1954, had its own DMZ. As for the rest, how you'd perform under fire? It's all speculation. Nobody knows until that first round cracks over your head. It's got little to do with yellow and everything with red.

"I played war games in Korea where the Ghost Battalion was wiped out because General MacArthur got caught with his pants down," Pete said. "I wasn't just some new recruit. I'd spent four years in this man's army. I knew what happened in Korea and it was bloody fucking awful! Three years of blood letting only to arrive back at the 38th Parallel, where it all began; high mountains, steep passes, deadly ravines, numbing cold and no winter gear."

"Deep kimchi." I nodded. Of all the U.S. Army's miscalculations, MacArthur's arrogant decision to send troops to the Yalu surpassed even Custer, that is until Iraq; Bush–Cheney & the WMD Gang. Deserters and draft dodgers, no matter what their political aspirations, shouldn't be allowed to send boys to war.

Pete really had no real idea that the flip side of Korean cold was Vietnam hot. Jungle rot, delta swamp, malaria, triple canopy, vines, bamboo, leeches, two steppers, dehydration, infection, was just as much the enemy. The country was carnivorous. It took a bite out of your ass every day.

"I remember watching President Johnson on TV," Pete said. "Hardly understood a word of that mush mouth, southern drawl. "Some men will fiiiiight and suum may dieeeeee . . ." and I wondered if he knew what the fuck he was doing sending us to fight Viet Cong. But when he asked, "*Whyyyyy must we take this painful roooooaaa-de?*" That was it. I thought, if you don't know who the fuck does?"

"The straw of indecision," I said. Maybe Pete *had* figured it out.

"I can't explain it," Pete said, "but as I looked over those reenlistment papers the hair stood up on the back of my neck. I thought of home, school and doing what I wanted for a change; G.I. Bill, commercial art, 9-5 and never busting hump again."

What the hell is this? Was Pete the kind of guy that spilled his guts until he blurted out some resolution? Was this his way of quantifying the cost of his choices or qualifying the trade off? Civilian life verses army. Wasn't that just trading one minefield for another?

"First Sarge said, 'Sign here and grab your gear,' which I figured was a life sentence, and I said, 'Thank you no, I gotta go!' I chose to muster out honorably from this man's army. Seven come eleven. I rolled the dice."

"What're the odds?" I asked.

"Better than Nam, I figured. So I went to the Class 6 store and bought a couple cases of beer, iced them down, wedged the cooler behind the bucket seat of my red GTO convertible. I bought a couple fifths of Jack Black. A good NCO always has a contingency plan."

"Drunk or super drunk," I said.

"I invented a new game," Pete said, "something like strip

poker. The rules were simple. Every time I finished a couple of beers I took off a piece of uniform or reached into my B-4 bag in the front seat and tossed a piece of army issue out the window. There were rules that I could amend or break when it suited, cause now I was the decider, not The Commander and Chief or the C-O or First Sergeant Luke or anyone else, not even the judge. I did my time. I particularly liked holding white T-shirts out the window, flags rippling. I liked feeling the wind tugging at my grip as I sped up the road; rip them out of my hand. Then I'd reach behind the seat, dip into the cool slosh of ice and retrieve another of Milwaukee's Best." Pete paused, raised his index finger. "I made up a little poem."

"It was clear, I remember, sunny day in September, cranked up the 4-2-4, clasped the stick, four on the floor, grabbed a gear and let 'er roar." He stripped off his belt, whipped it across the room and reached for another brew.

"It was nothing but blue sky when I left Columbus Georgia so I put the top down. As I cleared the front gate I picked up my Class A flat hat and sailed it like a frisbee at the MP. He ducked and fell back into the guard shack as I sped by." Pete chuckled. "Fuck 'em if they can't take a joke! Mind if I kick off my shoes?" He peeled off his socks and shuddered as his feet hit the cold tile.

"Dogs barkin'?"

"No, just feeling a little short of breath," Pete said. He extended both hands as if performing a sobriety test, fingers shaking. He rose, walked to the bathroom and shut the door. Minutes passed. A muffled moan and garden hose plash came from behind the door. Pete returned, shirt in hand.

"Zip your fly," I said.

"Is it hot in here?" He asked. "Where was I?" He popped another beer.

"Frisbee—MP, '*On the Road Again*,'" I sang. But I could definitely wait.

"After several hours I pulled into a deserted rest stop, kidneys screamin'," Pete said. "I looked forward to that first, long, luxurious piss. As I stood at the urinal a truck driver walked past and gave me the stink eye. 'Got a problem?' I said. He kept walking."

"Draining the swamp lightened the load but my head was spinning. In the mirror, I was down to a pair of pants, socks and dog tags. A vague memory flashed about stopping somewhere in South Carolina to remove my boots."

"It was back to my car for forty winks. I laid down in the back seat beneath a full moon with my feet draped over the trunk. I awoke with something tapping, gently rapping, tap, tap, tapping on my fender, could it be of female gender? Tapping on the 4-2-4," Pete said. "Rhyming couplets?"

"Not likely," I said.

"'Are you hurting, or deserting?' said the figure at my door. 'Sir, or Madam, it was drizzling, your forgiveness I implore. I am drunk and nothing more.' Then she pointed, self-anointed, at the cans that spread galore. 'What of those?' She vaguely whispered, 'All dead soldiers on the floor. Empty beer cans nothing more.' Then the drizzle, turned to showers, something I could not ignore. I absconded, up and bounded, started up the

4-2-4, put down the roof and let 'er roar."

"Quoth the Raven, Nevermore," I said.

Two could play this game. Wasn't I the poet laureate of PHS? I was torn between a desire to forget and urge to remember, truth my only stock and store.

Pete seemed as lost and implausible as a talking raven, sockless feet upon the floor, crushed tin soldiers spread before. It was obvious, him so heedless, what his drinking had in store. With each beer he drank so quickly, downed a case, maybe more. Then me thought his soul was rendered, stripped of pretense and surrendered, metamorphose nothing more. He reverted and converted into something you'd abhor, EL-ZE-X-Ray all his buddies, napalmed on that jungle floor, crispy critters tangled twisted, helicoptered out—no more. This, his vision and derision, like a movie seen before. We were young, but nevermore.

"My B-4 bag was stuffed with army gear," Pete said. "It slouched in the front seat against the door. As I rolled along I'd grab a helmet, shoe or boot and let it fly out the window. I watched in the rearview mirror as they bound after me like Buster, my dog."

"Must be ninety in here," Pete said. He drained the beer then doffed his pants.

"This ain't show and tell," I said. He sat and popped another.

"Clear headed now, I started drinking again as I reached the North Carolina line. The more I drank, the funnier things got, like the time we played mailbox baseball in Mintzer's

'53 Chevy. Bustin' mailboxes with that Louisville Slugger. What a rush, like I was finally breakin' out and nobody could stop me. The harder I swung the harder I laughed. The sight of those mailboxes exploding—letters floating down like confetti was a scream. Forget the friggin' baseball team. Try hitting a ninety-mile an hour fastball looking through these Coke bottles. I swung for the fences. Nailed it!"

"The judge said, 'Son, you have two choices, olive drab or prison gray.' 'I'll go with the green, sir, matches my eyes.' Judge said, 'Follow orders, learn the rules and Uncle Sam will treat you fine. Break the law—your ass is mine!' My father said, 'Serve us proud. Do your penance for the crime. Serve your country, most sublime.'"

"But now I was done with all that marching and saluting and orders and people telling me what to do and when to do it." Pete smiled. "It was time to get back to Old Virginny, '*where this old heart am long to go.*'"

"After several hours, beers and a couple shots I was singing and yelling out the window, '*Green Machine! Never* goin' back, never goin' back . . . to that *green mother fuck, green mother fuck!*'"

"Catchy," I said.

"My luck, I ran into a freak nor'easter around Fayetteville and the windshield fogged up so I turned on the defroster. I kept drinking beer after beer, only by now I was bone-ass naked except for my dog tags and a pistol belt around my waist."

"Kinda like now," I said.

"By the time I hit Chesterfield it was snowing to beat the

band. Every piece of clothing; Class A's, dress pants, shirts, ties, fatigues, boxer shorts, long johns, which I could have used at the moment; rucksack, field cap, compass, cunt cap, helmet, helmet liner, chin strap, and every scrap, remnant, and reminder of the Green Machine was gone. I was *free* at last!"

Pete chuckled. What memory or feeling had provoked him to hunt me down? He had served two years in an occupation army, came home and trained for war with the 1st Cavalry just in time to say *sayonara*. Fate, if you believe, dealt him a straight flush and in an odd reversal I drew a pair of deuces, won his slot in the Green Machine. But now he regretted cashing in his chips, choosing life over death.

I, on the other hand, anted up my youth. 'Deal,' I said. Who knew the game was rigged? Youth requires the illusion of choice. I disabused myself of the notion that I was self-sufficient and master of my fate. The domino theory has one axiom: Dominos in line continue falling until the last one falls. Uncle Sam sent me to Vietnam to prove it. But of course I'd disproved that theory many times in my youth after erecting zigzag patterns of dominos, odd shaped like Asian countries on a map. If one domino was slightly off line and didn't knock over the next one, then the rest were left standing. Any kid who played dominos had proof.

But you didn't have to be a kid to know the domino theory was screwed. If you were President Johnson all you had to do was watch the Fulbright Hearings on TV and listen to George Kennan, author of the doctrine of containment. 'The domino theory no longer pertains to Southeast Asia, if it ever did,'

Kennan said. 'Nor is there any reason to think Ho Chi Minh will be a puppet of China or Russia.' But instead of watching TV, Johnson called CBS and told them to shut it down. They played *I Love Lucy* reruns so the public wouldn't see the hearings. In summary, Kennan said, 'We can't achieve victory even with the best of wills,' and 'we should stop acting like an elephant who's seen a mouse.'

Now if they'd said prove the zigzag domino theory, maybe I'd been like Pete and said, hell no, I won't go! But I doubt it. You can wash out the smell of pissed pants after a firefight but the stain of not showing up would have been too much for me to bear.

Any protester who laid it all on the line had my full respect. At least they made a choice. But the indifferent souls who developed the Viet-guilt syndrome, because they didn't cross the line, are tattooed with indifference, forever more.

Pete missed the next biggest foreign policy fiasco after Cuba in our country's brief but bloody history. He missed LZ-X-Ray in all its savagery and death by fire, enemy and friendly. And now, I suspected, having lived the mundane life of a commercial artist, three failed marriages, corporate collapse, bankruptcy, no retirement and a passel of kids spread out over three states, he longed for the opportunity to die young, while immortal—be forever named on that beautiful black, granite, Vietnam Wall. Dominos tipped end-to-end.

"I was so drunk I forgot that all my civvies were in the B-4 bag," Pete said. "I got carried away, threw the baby out with the bathwater!" Pete's smile showcased a small gap in his front teeth and dimpled chin.

"About the time I crossed the Virginia line a polar vortex pushed down from Canada, collided with moist air pushing up from the gulf. My windshield fogged and my wipers clogged. I turned up the fan on the defroster but it wasn't working."

"By the time I pulled into the driveway on Treely, I could barely see out the windshield. It was early morning and I sat shivering, naked as a jaybird; correction, pistol belt and dog tags. The back seat was littered with casualties. I emptied the cooler and buried the dead under the snow. It was meet and right."

"The house was dark. I honked to wake my younger brother. I trusted he would bring some clothes out. But he'd heard I was coming home and ran away a few days before the storm blew in. I honked several more times and slowly the neighbors' lights came on but my house remained dark. I honked again and the window blinds in my parent's upstairs room fluttered, spread momentarily and snapped shut. I opened the door and stepped into the swirling snow and the crunch of ice beneath my feet. 'What the hell you waitin' for?' I said. They could kill the fatted calf later. I'm gettin' blue balls! After a couple of minutes the blinds raised slowly."

"There stood my father in his British, Home Guard uniform with corporal stripes. He surveyed me with a mixture of curiosity and pride. I'd never seen him in uniform before. He'd never talked about his service to Queen and Country—I never asked."

"I adjusted my glasses, as he disappeared from the

window. I straightened my pistol belt and looked down. Snow blew up my ass and shriveled my grapes. I gripped my dog tags—squeezed them 'til they cut my fingers. That my father was wearing corporal stripes gave me immense satisfaction and arousal, since I'd risen to the rank of buck sergeant."

Pete rose from his chair and came to attention, and as if on cue abruptly dropped trou. His eyes locked straight ahead as if readied for short arm inspection.

"*What the . . .!*" I said. "Sit the fuck down and put your drawers on!" But Tin Man froze, rusted after rain.

Memories of the army, LZ-X-Ray, dead buddies, father, judge, three failed marriages, job loss, bankruptcy, beer and more beer, must've overwhelmed him. It would take ten years on a couch and a case of Prozac to figure this out and I wasn't prepared for either.

"*Sit!*" I yelled.

Tin Man's arm pressed a can of Milwaukee's finest lubricant to his lips. Well oiled, he sat.

"My father, Corporal of the Home Guard," Pete said, "opened the door, marched front and center onto the porch, halted with that quick British high step, came to attention and saluted me with that open flat-handed British salute high on his forehead in conspicuous display. He wore a brown Corporal Jones Battle Dress uniform, pistol belt, ammo pouches, haversack and Bayonet frog—worn, I assumed, when he served during the London Blitz. I came to attention, presented arms with that crisp, knife edged, U.S. Army salute."

"'Welcome home,' the Corporal said. 'Well done!'

I snapped my best salute. 'You are to be congratulated on your outstanding service to your country and the United States Army. Now inside—to the quickstep. Wouldn't want you arrested first day home.' He saluted, performed an about face and marched into the house."

"I was snow covered," Pete said, "head and shoulders, but inside my chest was warm as a bed of coals. Didn't need clothes. That salute was the best thing I ever got from my old man." Pete sat, lost in thought. Clothes and cans littered the room.

"I missed my chance," he said. "I'll never know."

"*Wake the fuck up!*" I yelled in his ear. "The Green Fucking Machine!"

Pete gave a start and nudged his glasses flush on the bridge of his nose.

"Thing is, I don't remember it like that for a long time," he said.

"You ever smell a crispy critter? It ain't melted marshmallows!"

"*We Light the Way*." Pete shook his head. "What a joke."

"You lit your own fucking way! This romantic bullshit about dying with your buddies on LZ-X-Ray is *nuts!* Where the *fuck* you think *they'd rather be?*"

"And you?" He looked me straight in the eye.

"This has got nothing to do with me!" Bam! He'd flipped it around. I felt jujitsued by this crazy son-of-a-bitch. "Where the fuck would *I* rather be?"

"Thing of it is, when I was in the army," Pete said, "I hated all that spit and polish, formations, inspections, drill and ceremony, close-order drill, bivouac, long marches to the rifle range, chow, everything about it," he said. "I couldn't wait to get out."

"Got it."

"But now," Pete said, "I'm Commander of a VFW Post and Commandant of the Color Guard. We present the flag on Veteran's Day at the War Memorial; honor guards, bury the dead. I present the flag to grieving widows, take comfort in the crisp pleat of a Class A uniform, spit-shined boots, marching, sabers rattling, flags furling, twenty-one gun salute, fly-overs. They fill me up." He took a deep breath. "God help me, I love it."

"You think you can fill the emptiness with booze," I asked. "You come here for absolution?"

"You a priest?"

"I got nothin' for you." Something burned, whisky hot, in my throat. It was my old friend rage, bubbling. I cocked my right arm. I wanted to smash something, smash his nose for coming here and stirring shit up. A streetlamp spotlighted the last beer on the floor.

"Things show up," Pete said.

I looked around at the half painted walls, newly installed cabinets and tiled floor.

"People show up," he said.

"Thing is, I don't remember the people part for a long time."

"And yet . . ." Pete retrieved the last beer off the floor with a flourish, locked heels, snapped to attention, bent at the waist and presented Milwaukee's finest. "On behalf of the United

States Army and a grateful nation, please accept this beer as a symbol of our appreciation for your honorable and faithful service."

"I ain't dead yet," I said.

"Could have fooled me," Pete said. "Place feels like a mausoleum."

I cradled the beer in both hands, sipped hot bubbles, sweet and sour. The savory hops, bitter and zesty, complemented golden grain; coated my tongue for the longest time. I spit it out.

"Funny how memory flips around," Pete said.

"It's the first casualty of peace," I said. "But maybe truth has a way of doubling back around, making the puzzle fit together." I looked out the window and it was snowing. A thin white blanket covered the ground.

Pete swiped his brow with his forearm. "Haven't felt that heat since I came home," he said.

"The Home Guard," I said. Pete nodded absently.

"They also serve who stand in reserve," I said. Corny, but it sounded right. My anger cooled. Something welled up. Maybe this was as close to a welcome home as any Vietnam vet would ever get. 'On behalf of a grateful nation', turns out to be the gratitude of one citizen soldier. Not some synthetic, 'thank you for your service' platitude—but *one* deep, look in the eye; *one* resolute salute, from The Home Guard.

Up Pete gathered, clothes that mattered, scattered on the darkened floor, then the Home Guard, with his beer cans, empty now of poison lore—bowed, beguiling, ever smiling, sensed that life's a joyous chore.

"Funny how feelings flip around," I said. Cold wind gusted, snow fell, as Pete opened the door and stepped barefoot onto the covered porch.

"The Home Guard," Pete said. "Dad's Army. Got a nice ring to it." He winked and pushed up his glasses. We watched large wet flakes dissolve on the black pavement. All quiet on the southern front. He walked to his car, came to attention and broke into rhyme.

"Surely," Pete said, "I am grateful, thankful life is now restored. Seems no longer vain and aimless, all dead soldiers on the floor."

He saluted, flat hand open, fingers touched his naked brow, "*H'order H'arms!*" Pete commanded, "Warms the cockles of me heart."

I stood on the porch, snowflakes swirling and snapped a crisp U.S. Army knife-edged salute to Pete Star. The thought that he'd risen in rank to buck sergeant gave me immense satisfaction and arousal, since I'd climbed the ladder all the way to captain.

HELLO MY LITTLE FEAR OF WAR!

> Dharmakaya is the embodiment of the Dharma, always shining, enlightening trees, grass, birds and human beings, always emitting light . . . Moon in sky of utmost emptiness.
>
> Thich Nhat Hanh
> *Living Buddha, Living Christ*

Along with three other Vietnam veterans, Maxine Hong Kingston invited me to visit Thich Nhat Hanh, *Village de Pruniers,* in Southern France, 1994. Affectionately known as Thay, the Buddhist priest and Nobel Peace Prize nominee wrote books and poetry.

One evening during the month-long autumn retreat at Plum Village, Thay invited Maxine and the veterans to drink tea at his chalet, Thay's hootch—army lingo for hut. It was tucked nicely into dark recesses of a tree line, blending like a VC bunker. Ted Sexauer, an old airborne trooper, walked point as we traversed the tall grass. He goose-stepped with a cane ahead of me. We walked from the veteran's hootch, a small billet with open bay, eight beds and a bathroom. Ever vigilant, I surveyed the narrow path and tall weeds. We shared an aversion, chiseled in bone, about walking trails in open fields. How to practice living in the present moment, wonderful moment, when a voice said, *never walk a trail*? Even after hours of sitting and walking meditation, some things triggered caution.

Thay lived several kilometers from Plum Village in a hermitage so his chauffer, Sister Chang Khong drove him. The crisp fall air slowed the septuagenarian's pace to that of an escargot.

Promoted and produced by BBC, Maxine had been invited for a series of interviews. The documentary, *Stories My Country Told Me*, featured writers and teachers journeying across boundaries. Desmond Tutu, first black Archbishop, traveled from Cape Town to Johannesburg. Eric Hobsbawm, pre-eminent Marxist historian, trekked through Yugoslavia, and Eqbal Ahmad, anti-war activist journeyed from Pakistan to India.

Maxine, well-known author, activist and educator, had recently returned from her small, ancestral village in China. "The people were poor and accommodations spare," Maxine said. "I left money to be shared among my ancestors." She was dismayed and annoyed by the experience. After flying home, she received a letter from a woman who said she hadn't received her share. Maxine didn't cherish the idea of returning to such poverty and pettiness so she chose to 'return' to Plum Village, for the very first time.

Anthony Wall, the producer, said, "If Plum Village is where your heart is, then that's where we'll film you."

The phone rang and Maxine's soft voice said, "Can you go

with me to Plum Village for autumn retreat?"

"France?" We'd been out of touch since the last veteran's retreat in upstate New York, Omega Institute. The retreat center, built in the rolling hills of Hudson Valley, promoted solemnity and mindfulness.

"A month of Noble Silence, sitting and walking meditation, dharma talks, strict vegetarian diet, and no spirits."

"*A Clean Well Lighted Place*," I said.

"It could be intoxicating."

The unexpected invite came during my move into a newly rehabbed home. Living from pillar to post for five years, I relished the idea of having my own place. The small Spanish style hacienda resembled something out of a spaghetti western. I'd spent spring and summer working on the fixer-upper. The roof leaked, floors buckled and walls were dark with mold. A friend bought it in foreclosure from a Vietnam vet whose life had spiraled into the dumpster.

His uncle had seen the need for cheap housing for veterans returning home after World War II. Commodities were still rationed and lumber was in short supply but cement, rocks, sand and rebar were plentiful. His idea? Cast the entire house in reinforced concrete. The surface, inside and out, was troweled and painted beige to soften edges. The cramped living space, though appealing to the eye, took a toll on the body.

Summer, the walls and rebar absorbed the blazing Virginia sun. During sweat soaked nights the walls radiated like a kiln. Come winter, the concrete walls absorbed the cold.

The cement slab and wood floors wore on the bones. Living in the bunker was like camping in a quarry. Concrete stairs led down to a fortified basement that could withstand any attack, foreign or domestic.

"We'll meet in Paris on the West Bank," Maxine said. "The BBC will pay for everything, travel and lodging. I've asked Jerry, Ted, Jimmy and last but not least, you.

"Francais." I recalled backpacking Europe as one of the joys of youth. I savored the memory of sitting on a bench in front of Notre Dame—fresh baguette, cheese, wine, girl watching.

It would be special to revisit Gertrude Stein's old haunts, The Montparnasse Quarter, *une generation perdue,* expatriate writers gathered on the West Bank after WWI. 'That's what you all are, the Lost Generation,' Stein said to Hemingway. 'You've witnessed the war to end all wars.' Not really.

I'd been feeling temporarily lost, but never disoriented. Perhaps, after three generations, two wars and a police action, a new generation of veterans, writers and poets would coalesce in those same old haunts or discover new ones.

"What about the Found Generation," I said. But that story, sixteen hundred Chinese youth migrating to Paris after WWI, had already been written. Irony or coincidence, take your pick. What had been the difference between Lost and Found, East and West, during the Roaring Twenties? Driven by apathy and detachment, Westerners lost all hope and faith in society, while Easterners were driven by optimism and purpose.

"One breath at a time," Maxine assured. She'd been smitten by the Beat Generation, Kerouac, Ginsburg and Burroughs, and for all intents and purposes, identified with Dharma Bums.

"I'm in," I said. One thing for sure, Vietnam vets had been tossed into the lost and found. This was my opportunity to answer lingering questions about Buddhism and mindfulness.

Remembering Hemingway's warning in *A Moveable Feast*, 'Never go on trips with anyone you don't love,' I figured this was like going to a new play. You couldn't fall in love with the characters if you didn't attend the matinee. I catalogued the group of veterans I'd met at Omega.

Ted, a gifted poet, showed up at Omega for a Veteran's Retreat sponsored by *The Community of Mindfulness*. He was lanky and limped from a degenerative hip, exacerbated by parachute landing falls and leaping from choppers during combat assaults. As a line medic he was always heavy with medical bag, web gear, rifle and ruck. It had taken a toll.

"Sometimes pilots couldn't tell if they were two feet or ten off the ground in elephant grass." Ted's chiseled cheekbones, square jaw, and thick hair resembled a middle aged Hemingway, sans gut. An erudite contrarian with curly mane, he was always in search of the golden mean.

"Airborne, sergeant," could well have been his mantra. He gestured with his cane, amused by the fact he'd volunteered for all that crazy shit. An indomitable spirit and steely will had wrecked his frame.

"Maybe it was all that disc compression, torqueing, slamming to the ground like a sack of potatoes," I said.

I liked him instantly, his brash truth telling in the face of all that was unreasonable. "I went to Vietnam to have something to write about," he said matter-of-factly during a workshop. Another time he was the sacrificial lamb, "I stayed in Vietnam so my brother didn't have to go." In the end, it was more choice than chance.

Ted's poetry was *imagist* on the order of William Carlos Williams. Like Williams he'd been called to the healing arts, humped the Rod of Asclepius. "After Nam I worked in ER and studied for med school. All that pressure, trying to save people I hadn't saved, kept trying to save. I tried to fit the pieces back together. The harder I worked the more it flew apart."

I'd come to the same conclusion after years in Special Forces Reserves. Deep down I believed if I trained men to survive the next war, it would serve as a do-over. But then I'd been addicted to risk and rush, daring do; jumping from planes, boats, taking trains; hopscotching the globe. It took years of magical thinking to reconfigure my war. In the end, I lost.

Ted loved word play, coined the term "Dharma Nazi" for all the strident, born again Buddhists–Jugendbund in former lives. We'd experienced many of the same things, OCS, Airborne School, Special Forces Q School, and Vietnam. I'd graduated from OCS and been assigned to SOG, Studies and Observation Group. He was originally assigned to the 1st Civil Affairs/ 3rd Special Forces Group, Fort Bragg after he graduated from a nine-month Serbo Croat School in Pasadena. He volunteered for Airborne School, and Infantry OCS. Whereas I graduated OCS, Ted reconfigured his goals and ideals.

"I resigned during the seventeenth week after a kind of awakening. The moral questions about Vietnam, particularly the civilian death toll didn't make sense. I couldn't order someone to do what I couldn't do." I admired him not only for listening to his conscience but acting on it. He reenlisted for three years, with a bonus, for Special Forces Medic Training and received $2000 because of his foreign language skills. "That was a lot of money back then and I shouldn't have gotten it [money] because I'd enlisted for a different MOS."

"I thought, maybe I could save some sliver of the indigenous population of Vietnam or wounded soldiers, learn about war at a distance, deal with its aftermath. I was dead wrong about that." The burgeoning idealist had a big heart. He had the right stuff, but he suffered from bad timing, luck or both. The yearlong medic's course was as mentally and physically challenging as any the army had to offer. He learned surgical techniques, how to deliver babies and seal sucking chest wounds. But after graduating from Phase II at Fort Sam Houston, he and a few of his classmates drove across the Mexican boarder to Nuevo Laredo—sought relief, bought a kilo of pot.

"Seems to me the same guy that sold the pot turned us in," Ted said, with wry indifference. "He gets a triple payday—sells us the pot, collects a juicy reward for turning in gringos, and they probably gave him the pot back." He shrugged. "Whatcha gonna do?"

Ted was kicked out of Special Forces—stripped of his 91B MOS—Do Not Pass Go (already collected $200); flew directly to 90th Repo Depot, Long Binh, Vietnam. "At the repo depot I looked up on the board where they post orders and magically there was a 91B behind my name. I was a medic again. No one said a thing, *Kazam!* I'm a full fledged medic so I'm assigned to the 571 Medevac Unit in Phu Bai."

Our AO's, Quang Tri Province, Hue and Phu Bai, Ashau Valley, were similar, though my stomping ground was across the fence. When we talked it was like a Spock mind meld. He didn't have to explain anything nor did I. We just knew, and that was an amazing comfort and connection.

After flying medevac for a year, he extended his tour with Alpha Company, 4th Battalion, 173rd Airborne. He humped steep slopes and sharp ridgelines around Bong Son. He knew the sweat and stink of lugging a ruck in dense broadleaf jungle, where Charlie so ably surprised.

I'd landed at CCN, FOB #4 in Da Nang, next to Marble Mountain, and was further assigned to Mobile Launch Team One, MLT-1, near the Laotian border. It wasn't far from Khe Sanh. I extended with the *Top Secret*, SOG unit, whose AO was Laos and North Vietnam. We launched 6-8 man recon teams, RT's, into highly classified, cross/border operations, surveil the Ho Chi Minh Road. Team losses, at times, were universal.

Ted earned his tag, "Doc" because he wasn't just some numb nuts 91Bravo with 12-week training. A skilled medic, with extensive training, he had a year of experience saving lives in the ER. "Grunts held me up, believed that I could keep them alive long enough to get them out on a chopper," he said. "And god help me, I let them."

"The biggest lie came naturally and I used it often, 'You're going to be alright,' along with 'You're going home,'" he said. "They all went home, sometimes in a bag."

His best friend, K.C. Nokes, was killed by pilot error shortly before he DEROS'd. The senseless death by friendly fire, stung him hard and was the tipping point. That event jump-started what was later diagnosed as bipolar disorder (atypical).

Another cast member, Jimmy Jenko, was also a medic. Served with C Company, 27th Battalion, Wolfhounds. I was partial to Jimmy's soft-spoken ways. My father had been posted to the Wolfhounds as a raw recruit in 1939. I'd grown up with stories about James Jones characters, Pruitt or the sadistic sergeant in, *From Here to Eternity*. My father, a buck sergeant machine gunner, slipped into the mess hall for breakfast, December 7, 1941, minutes before the attack on Pearl Harbor. When the attack began he broke into the armory and hauled a water-cooled machine gun atop his barracks and fired at Zero's during the attack. Burt Lancaster played the role in the movie.

Jimmy was small in stature, wild-eyed, but mild mannered with spiked hair. His eyes darted around the room like a humming bird; hovering never landing. His quick wit and disarming smile camouflaged wounds. He had tended the wounded during Renegade Woods, April 2-6, LTC George Armstrong Custer III, commanding. Surrounded by Indians, he ran out of morphine serrates, gauze and IV's during the bloody battle. The stacked bodies kept him alive. He kept his scalp, but his spirit was wounded.

After Vietnam he chose thirteen years of solitary confinement; night watchman Alcatraz. He never wore a gun. His Wolfhound growl warned trespassers who mistakenly ventured onto the island. He was more ascetic than troglodyte.

The anti-hero, Jerry Crawford, had been a ranger with D Company, 51st Infantry. Bald on top, his hair was pulled back into a samurai bun with wire-rimmed glasses. He wore black leather, rode a Hog in search of windmills. He was haunted by the ghost of a woman guerilla he'd killed—after she'd killed his buddy. He'd been a non-commissioned officer in the army and he bitched incessantly. He railed against authority, didn't trust it, questioned everything and was hard of hearing. A pure non-conformist, he'd finished a graduate program in education at the University of Southern Maine, but didn't like teaching.

Maxine, husband Earll, four Vietnam vet's and the BBC crew linked up at the Charles de Gaulle Airport, Paris. We piled into a van and drove to the Left Bank, Montparnasse, Beaujolais Day, always the third Thursday of November.

That evening the BBC crew treated us to a scrumptious dinner at one of Hemingway's favorite haunts. My taste buds took great delight sampling baked quail, fresh roasted peas, pomfritz, leafy green salad, fresh bread slathered in butter and pitchers of vin de primeur, Beaujolais nouveau, aromatic and slightly sweet that washed down easy as Kool-Aid.

The next day we streaked across the countryside in a sleek TVG train at 225 miles per hour, smooth as a magic carpet. The bullet nosed train resembled a jet sled. Looking down, the ground swept past in a blur, as though speeding back in time. I imagined my 13th great-grandfather, Edvard Bumpass, sitting beside me amazed we were covering more in an hour than he could in a month. The sweet irony of a journey of peace had its allure. France, a colonial power, dragged the U.S. into Vietnam. Then too, my Grandpa, a Huguenot, fled in 1599 after religious wars with the Catholics broke out. He arrived in England under the growing hostility of the Roman Catholic State, after Henry IV issued the Edict of Nantes. Thirteen generations later, I'd come full circle.

Edvard sailed on the second passage of the *Fortune* and landed in 1621 at Plymouth Rock. Years later one of his descendants migrated south to Virginia and founded the small town of Bumpass, near home. I thought of Cole Morton, marine officer, I'd met at Omega, and how our fates were intertwined. An altar boy in youth, he sang baritone for the sangha, during Omega retreats:

Castles are sacked in war
Chieftains scattered far
Truth is but a fixed star
Ai-leen a-roon

Overly proud of my Norwegian ancestry, I was ambivalent about my thin strand of French DNA until I met Cole. In search of Edvard at the Historical Society in Plymouth Mass I found out how tightly our strands had been woven. Flipping through the Fortune's manifest, I was shocked and pleased to find Cole's great-grandfather and mine had crossed that brutal passage together. They'd slept side by side crammed in the hold. Reading, touching that manifest gave me immense satisfaction and wonderment about how time and events conspire to weave strands of history into one colorful duvet.

Trusting it would all be puzzled together, I was buoyed by that same sense of spiritual connection I'd found on the grounds of the Culinary Institute of America, Rhinebeck. I had eagerly accepted an invitation, joined an impetuous pilgrimage, in order to pay homage to Teilhard de Chardin, a brilliant geologist, philosopher, writer and defrocked Jesuit priest. Now, in search of *Big Mind,* a Zen tradition, I hoped Thay would confirm Teilhard's imagination and inspiration, divine guidance.

The Frenchman's teleological theory of man was based on the inevitable evolution of all thought and being converging at the *Omega Point*. All matter, he theorized, had an inherent compulsion to arrange itself into more and more complex groupings that exhibited higher and higher levels of consciousness. Atoms, cells, animal, man, galaxies, the universe, strove collectively to order themselves towards higher states of consciousness, and ultimately coalesce at the *Omega Point*.

Was that why I'd been drawn to the Veteran's Retreat at Omega, where all these characters merged? Since there are no coincidences, it must have been synchronicity. Here I sat, speeding through space/time with a coalition of willing radicals; mentally, physically and spiritually bound for our next way station. Perhaps generation trouvee, bound by time and circumstance of war, hurtled towards the promise of higher consciousness. Maybe Plum Village was the intersection?

We transferred in Libourne, a quaint town in the winemaking capital of Gironde, southwest France. The stone tip of a Gothic spire pointed at the faint, empty outline of the moon, pinned against a brilliant blue sky. We stretched and mounted an older model train, small, similar to those in Vietnam. The occupation of French Indo China, Vietnam, had been built, sociologically and financially, on its rather advanced rail system.

As we pulled from the station my head jerked, followed by the metallic clang of couplers gripping the cars. They creaked and moaned as we eased from the station, straining for a head of steam. The large windows allowed me to soak in the countryside, golden fields awash, spinning clouds, black crows rising from Van Gogh's grand canvas. By the time we arrived in Sainte Foy-La-Grande, my senses were sated.

I stood alone on the deck of Thay's hootch awaiting the start of the filming. Leaves shimmered in the fading sunlight as I collected my thoughts. By tradition each member of the group would ask the Zen master one question. Fortunately, due to my singular focus, one was all I had.

Inside, Maxine and the veterans sat with Thay. The BBC

film crew had set and reset the lights and camera until the hyper-focal distance and angles were perfectly struck. I peered through the window. Black electrical cords circumscribed the group; enclosed the living mandala.

I took my place in the circle. Thay sat erect, hands folded in lap. A monk filled teacups and passed them around. Thay waited until everyone got one. How had such a disparate coalition of warriors and peaceniks arrived in this space?

"It is a miracle we are drinking tea, together," Thay said.

But there had been a tear in the cosmic fabric that morning. The sangha had risen early for sitting meditation in the main hall and afterward each walked alone through the countryside. Wisps of fog purled above rolling fields of bent stalks and gnarly vines. Jerry Crawford heard gunshots that morning. Maxine wrote about it in *Fifth Book Of Peace*.

" . . . because I was walking this morning, thinking calmly and then the shooting started and it frightened me. I have trouble breaking through that fear. I have trouble being calm when I have chaos going round in my head all the time. Perhaps this is not a question, its simply to let you know that I'm trying very hard to be mindful but it doesn't work . . . it doesn't always work for me."

Flashback, I thought. It was evident from his anguished look that Jerry heard shots and it kicked up a vivid memory.

Suddenly Sister Chang got what Jerry meant, that there was actually shooting (shotgun) this morning. "Oh, I understand. I hear him. My insight—it was the hunter's gunshots."

She continued, "I see his point, he said he heard the

shooting of the hunter and because of that (it) revive(s) the fear of the war in the past. And so if you can say: 'Hello, my little fear of the war, my experience again, you go back, we are in a safe area. [I'm] Here's [in] Plum Village. [This] Is not Vietnam in war. Here is Thay; here is Maxine, here's all your friends, and we are practicing mindfulness.'"

My face flushed hot when she said 'my *little* fear of war.' Thay had just lectured on suffering the wounds of war in a dharma talk. Didn't she understand that safety and trauma were incompatible?

"Ah, suffering is also very important," Thay said. "You need to suffer in order to learn from your suffering. We may suffer uselessly, but if we look deeply into our suffering, we can learn a lot from that."

So you need to suffer in order to learn from your suffering—but we may suffer uselessly. The enigmatic shell game drove me to distraction. If his talks were designed so the pea was never under the husk, then all this running commentary, big answers to big questions, was similar to *Midrash*; never definitively answered. Any master easily sidestepped queries from novitiates.

> *Form is emptiness, emptiness is form / Form is not other than emptiness / Emptiness is not other than form. / In emptiness there is neither form, nor feeling, nor perception / Nor mental formations, nor consciousness, / No ill-being / no cause of ill being. / No end of ill-being, and no path / No understanding / No attainment.*

The point *was* that Jerry had a flashback. He didn't

have control over his reaction, no matter how many breaths he took, how slow he walked, or how hard he did or didn't try to control it. The reaction to the gunshot was an autonomic response made by the body to protect itself; flinching as a bug hits your eye.

Jerry had been in firefights. His body was wired differently. His reptilian brain and limbic system detected danger a nanosecond before it registered in his conscious brain. His body knew he was in mortal danger and it responded. It pumped adrenaline and other hormones throughout his body. The visceral sensations from queasiness to panic in his chest were designed to get him moving in a firefight. Fight or flight, before the rational brain had a chance to take a breath and say, 'Hello, my little fear.'

Thay threw it in reverse, "Don't try very hard to be mindful [Jerry]." He laughed. "Just be in touch with what is there, the people around you, trees, sky, leaves, everything around you. Just be in touch with them and then you will be healed, you will have peace. You will have joy. Don't try too hard to be mindful at all, to be something else—just be yourself. That's what I practice also."

Thay had missed the point. Jerry *was* being himself. Thay's physiological understanding of flashbacks didn't match up with mindfulness training, here and now. Body memory informs and supersedes the mind during a flashback. Jerry wanted nothing more than to sit, walk, or meditate, be in his body, without his hyper-vigilant mind racing ahead like Road Runner.

The BBC crew signaled one minute warning. I caught Thay's eye. It was my one and only chance.

"Will Buddhism and Christianity merge into one?" I asked.

"Let's have a cup of tea," Thay said. His soft rebuke said, *enough*. The BBC wrapped and Sister Chang chauffeured him back to the hermitage.

A disillusioned Dharma Bum stepped onto a cold, clean, moonlit deck. I shuddered; wondered if I'd missed the yab-yum ritual. I'd journeyed all this way to rummage through the lost and found box and it was empty. I had no answers, no understanding and it was time for tea.

White moon filled empty sky. Transfixed by the shimmering reflection in double-paned windows, my face, hands, and threadbare jeans quivered like atoms under a microscope.

AUTHOR BIO

D.M. Thompson served in Vietnam with MAC-V SOG, Studies and Observation Group, 1968-70. His assignments as Hatchet Force platoon leader, Recon Team Leader (One Zero), Covey Rider, coupled with staff assignments as Assistant S-2, S-3 and Launch Site Commander, gave him a broad and discerning view of SOG operations. He was called back to serve in 11th Special Forces Group, 1978-86. His first published story, an excerpt from his novel, *Marble Mountain* (working title), appeared in Maxine Hong Kingston's *Veterans of War, Veterans of Peace*, 2006. His work of creative non-fiction, *Marble Mountain Redux*, based on his return to Vietnam in 1994 and reunion with SOG brothers in 2012, is scheduled for release 2018. D.M. Thompson is a Life Member of Special Operations Association and Special Forces Association. He lives in Richmond, VA.

www.dmtpress.com

Made in the USA
Lexington, KY
05 June 2018